I FALL APART

i fall apart

KENZIE HART

Editor: Jovana Shirley, Unforeseen Editing, www.unforeseenediting.com

Eclipse Publishing, Inc.
Madeira Beach, FL

ISBN: 978-1-946793-44-7

To a boy with blues eyes
who could have had my heart,
but broke it instead.

"It was just a kiss."
That's what my friends told me.
But they couldn't really understand.
It was a kiss.
A kiss that made me feel like I could fly and crash all at once.
A kiss that set my body aflame.
A kiss that eventually tore me apart.
A kiss that wrecked my whole world.
It was a kiss alright.
One that changed *everything*.

1.

Walking into the pub
I feel buzzed
And happy
It's the fourth bar of the night
And our first night in Ireland.
I'm out with three other girls,
Moving happily from one place to the next
Exploring the cobblestone streets of this seaside town
Overlooking the Atlantic.
We're here through our university,
Participating in a summer exchange program
I'm taking three courses,
Two history
One literature
And classes start Monday,
Giving us the weekend to settle in,
And get acquainted with the area
And to my new friends
That means getting acquainted with the locals,
And their beer.
They don't want the excitement of our first night here to end
And I have to admit,

Neither do I.
I've spent all spring saving up for this summer.
The bar is packed
It's packed with people dancing,
Standing.
Couples seated in cozy corners.
Friends at booths, laughing.
It's loud
And it's fun
Getting to know the girls
Listening to the music
Sipping a drink and toasting to everything we can think of
But things start to change.
They start to slur,
And giggle.
Their faces becoming lax and their movements slowed.
The evening is winding down,
And we all agree to leave,
Ten more minutes, and then we will go.
I think I've heard that three times now.
But it's fun.
Finally, we all agree that it is actually time to leave
And I think I'm the first one to make the move
To head for the exit
I'm already halfway out the door
When I hear one of them call my name
"We've made friends." She giggles at me
Thrusting her hand out to a group of boys
Thrusting her hand out to you.

I look at you
Not really looking.
Not really seeing.
We were supposed to be leaving
But my friends plead with me
Their eyes going wide
So I move to the corner
Standing beside you
Watching as they talk and flirt
With the new boys they've met
Your friends.
And you stand beside me.
Holding a drink in your hand.
Tall and silent.
Silent in the corner.
Silently staring at me.
It makes my chest pound
It makes my stomach flutter
And it makes me uncomfortable.
"Hi, I'm…" you whisper,
Leaning closer,
Those blue eyes gazing down at me.
"Hi," I say, lightly shaking your hand,
Not meeting your gaze
All I can look at is the floor.
You shift at my side,
And I feel your hand find its way onto my back as you lean in
to speak.
"What is your—"

Is all you get out
Because your hand on my back causes me to jump
I don't introduce myself
I don't look at you
I run straight for the bathroom
Standing there
Staring at myself in the mirror
And I don't even want to meet my own gaze.
What is wrong with me?
Why am I so nervous?
Why is a stranger getting to me so much?
I wash my face clean
Trying to clear my head.
Just relax.
I walk back out
And it's as if nothing has changed.
Everyone is in the same spot.
You're still standing in that corner.
But your gaze isn't on them.
You aren't drawn into their conversation.
You're standing there
Looking at me
Staring at me
And I can't do anything other than stare back
I smile as I move into the circle
Back into the corner,
Back next to you.
And I try not to look at those blue eyes again
I try to focus on the conversation

But I'm drawn to you
I'm drawn to those eyes
And I give in.
I turn slightly
Bringing my gaze up to your face.
You have high cheekbones
Light scruff and dark hair
Atlantic-blue eyes
My insides feel frozen
Staring at you
And instead of feeling uncomfortable
I feel transfixed.
"We're going to move this party to a booth, you coming?"
one of the girls asks.
The last of my friends
And his
To be standing in front of me.
I flip my gaze to her,
And I don't actually have an answer
She just looks at me, and laughs lightly
"We will be over there," she says, pointing to a booth,
Raising her eyebrows at me before walking away.
I have to walk away from you
So I start to follow her
But I stop
Standing there in the middle of the pub
And turn back to you
To look at you
You're still leaning against the wall

Staring at me
Now grinning at me
And your warm smile makes me not want to move
Because you see me.
It's not just the surface you're looking at
It's like when you look at me,
You're looking into me.
All I can see is your fitted black shirt and those blue eyes.
You push off the wall, stepping closer
I open my mouth, thinking I should say something
But nothing comes out
I close it.
Because I'm not really thinking.
I'm feeling.
And I don't know how to place this feeling.
You shift closer to me, those blue eyes looking down into
mine
And then you kiss me
You kiss my lips
You kiss my neck
You taste faintly of beer
Of a cigarette
And it's intoxicating
I pull away, flushed
Shocked.
I'm not someone who kisses strangers
But you don't feel like a stranger
It feels like I've known you forever
Like our souls have crossed paths before

Intertwined together in some past time,
Some former life
Because I feel like I know you.
You smile at my flushed face
And then kiss me again
Deeper
More insistent.
I move my hands to your chest
And your fingers press against my back
Your mouth opening wider until your tongue slips in
Until goosebumps are covering all of my skin.
We kiss for a long time
Until finally you pull away.
"Would you like a drink?" you ask
Pushing your hand through your dark hair.
I nod
I'm not thirsty
I don't need a drink
But I need to move.
You grab onto my hand
Lacing your fingers in mine and lead me to the bar.
You set down your drink,
"Water is fine," I finally speak.
Your back is turned to me
Speaking to the bartender
Then just as quickly you are again facing me
Those blue eyes pinning me between you and a wall
"Tell me something about you," I breathe out the words,
Desperate for a moment to clear my head.

You shrug at me

"I don't know," you say,

Almost blushing

"I am who I am."

"And who exactly is that?"

I can't help the smile on my face.

"I enjoy movies. And music. I have a shit job," you laugh.

"But you stay?"

You just nod.

"And you. Who are you?"

Your eyebrows raise in question.

"I'm here for the summer. For university."

You smile at me,

A big smile

And it makes my chest pound

"You're smart, aren't you?"

I just shrug, but I think my smile gives it away.

"I try."

Your chest rises and falls with your light laugh,

And my eyes slip from your face down to your shirt.

It moves further down to your arms

Full of tattoos.

Full of hidden meanings.

"This one is for my family," you say, pointing one out.

"I miss them."

"Where are they?"

"They are in my home country, Montenegro. I am here on a work visa."

I look back up into your eyes.

And I find sadness
I can tell you miss them
And before I know what I'm doing,
I'm holding onto your arm,
Touching that tattoo.
I can't look into your eyes
Each time I meet your gaze, I feel lost.
Lost in your eyes,
Lost in something I don't understand.
Both of your hands come up against my cheeks
Cupping them in your fingers
And you pull me to your lips.
You press into me
With so much emotion
That my body folds into you.
Your hands on my face,
It feels natural
It feels right.
And then your tongue moves against my lips.
Your breath is hot in my mouth,
And your hands move to press into my back.
Pressing me against you.
My fingers slip up to your shoulders
My nails digging into them
Moving across your collarbone and into your hair.
Everything is perfect
Everything is easy
The kisses are intense
But not forced

Your fingers press into me
But they aren't pushing me
We're at a crossroads of giving and taking,
Going fast but being gentle.
But then your lips leave mine
And you trail them down over my jaw to my neck
Pulling against my skin.
My whole body shudders,
And my stomach tightens at the sensation.
You pull back,
Taking my pink face into your hands again
Just staring at me
Staring at my face
Into my eyes.
I try to turn my head away
But you won't let me
And I feel like my chest might burst.
"Alright, kids! Closing time."
A man comes through the pub, shouting
Gathering everyone up.
Your eyes still don't leave mine
Then you pull out your phone
Holding it in one hand,
Grabbing onto mine in the other
"I will call you tomorrow if you'd like? We can go for food.
Coffee?"
I see uncertainty in your eyes
And I don't like it.
I nod

Smiling
Taking your phone into my fingers
"Of course. Yes."
"Yes?" You smile back at me
Your eyes beaming
And you grab onto my face
Pulling me to your lips one more time.

2.

"How do you take your coffee?"
You ask me this question as we take a seat at a café in town.
"Black is fine." I smile at you.
You nod
And then you go inside to the counter to order.
When you come back,
Sitting down next to me
My stomach twists in my belly
Just the sight of you has my whole body feeling high
"You look very beautiful today," you say.
Taking my hand into yours
Running your fingers across my skin.
It makes goosebumps rise down my arms.
"Thank you." I blush.
You smile,
And I notice a small dimple form.
I want to run my hand across it
Across those lips
And the thought makes me blush more,
Sitting here, thinking those things about you.
"Your skin gives you away."
You laugh

And pull me to your lips.
You kiss me easily,
Your warm lips locking onto mine.
With your hand against my jaw,
I hold onto your arm.
You don't deepen the kiss,
You don't hold it for too long.
And when you pull back,
I think my eyes stay closed for a minute too long.
"So you will attend university here?" you ask
Smiling next to me.
I nod.
"I'll be taking three courses over summer.
How did you end up here?" I ask.
Your take out a cigarette
Lighting it across the table from me
Taking a sip of your coffee
"I came for work.
At home,
In my country,
I had trouble finding a job.
So now, I'm here."
I nod
Watching you exhale smoke.
"But I like it here.
The ocean is beautiful.
If you'd like, I will take you to one of my favorite places.
Down to the beach."
"That sounds nice."

You ash your cigarette,
Slipping your hand across the table,
Wrapping your fingers around mine.
Your eyes sparkle,
And I know my eyes match yours
"From the moment I saw you,
I couldn't take my eyes off of you."
You squeeze my hand
"It was unexpected," I admit.
It took me by surprise.
You take me by surprise.
"But good I hope?" you question.
And I nod at you.
"It was perfect."
Just as everything is perfect today
Sitting here in the warm sun
Drinking coffee
Holding your hand
Watching you watch me.
It's all perfect.
And you're perfect too.

3.

Your fingers slip through mine, rubbing against my skin.
We watch as the waves crash ashore.
Their cold weight shifting the rocks beneath them.
They flow inward, and then are ripped back out.
An endless cycle.
An endless flow.
"I like this beach. It's different from the ones back home," I
comment.
You look at me, your nose pink from the chill.
"And I've always dreamt of seeing a soft, sandy beach," you
grin.
"I like the darkness of this one."
The sky is clouded gray.
The sunlight filters lightly through.
"It is beautiful. The darkness."
You pull me closer, wrapping your arm around me.
My thick coat keeps me warm
But the heat rising from within has more to do with you.
"Thank you for bringing me here."
You told me it was your favorite place.
You couldn't place why exactly
My theory is you like the chaos

The power of the ocean
It makes you feel connected
Yet, you have no control.
With everything worthwhile in life, there are two sides to the
greatness.
One side which gives you everything
The other side which shows you aren't in control of it
Which is why experiencing it is so beautiful.
"This is where I find my joy," you reply.
I tuck my body closer to you.
I move my lips to your cold neck
Goosebumps travel up my arms.
Your skin tastes salty.
Misted with sea air
But I still find you under it
Smoke and sunlight.
How someone can smell like sunlight, I'm not sure.
But you do.
"I think I could find my joy here too," I reply.
But I could find my joy anywhere
In any place
As long as I'm with you.
You run your hands through my hair as I move my lips to
yours
And you kiss me back
Your hot breath warming every part of me
Your tongue dancing across my lips
But I pull away.
"What do you think about when you come here?"

I want to know more about you
I want to know every little detail about who you are.
Your brows furrow slightly
"I think of many things. Mostly these things we cannot
describe in words."
I lean back
"Like what?"
"What it all means. Us. Creation."
You shrug
"I think of many things. But here, at the beach, I think of my
family. My home."
"Will you go back soon?"
My heart drops with your saddened gaze.
"I will see them soon, I hope. Maybe this fall."
Your blue eyes look back at me,
A twinkle coming into them
And you smile
You smile at me.
"Come, I will take you to dip your toes in the water now,"
you grin.
You stand up, grabbing my hand in the process, pulling me
with you.
"Isn't it freezing?" I question.
Your lips pull at the corners
A hint of teeth escapes your closed smile
You just nod, letting out a laugh.
"You will feel completely refreshed after, I promise."
You promise.
So I go with you.

Stripping off my sandy shoes on the rocky shore
Running down like lunatics into the freezing water
Just to run back out again as quickly.
But when we get back to our shoes,
Your chest is rising, and you aren't hiding your smile
anymore,
And my eyes wander over your chest
Down to our interlaced hands,
And I feel like I can't breathe.

4.

Walking back into my room
My new friends attack me with questions
With excitement
"How was your date?"
"Where did you go?"
"Is that what you wore?"
"This is so romantic!"
"I wish I could have a summer romance," one pouts.
"You've just been for coffee?"
"He hasn't taken you on a proper date yet?"
"Where does he work?"
"Does he have a good job?"
"When are you seeing him again?"
"Is he taking you to dinner?"
"What will you wear?"
"Can you believe the homework for this class?"
"I wonder what I should wear out this weekend."
"We should go back out to the pubs."
The questions are constant
But exciting
And invasive
The conversation ever-changing

I try to keep up
I try to follow along
But my mind moves to you
To how much I really like you
And my whole body tingles
Happiness coursing through me
So I let them talk
I let them sit on my bed
Asking me questions
Planning out our week
Giggling about our teachers
And it makes me smile
Everything about this trip,
This town
This summer
These girls
Makes me smile.

5.

I feel like you're the only one who understands.
I don't care about impressions
I don't care about *the date*
Where we eat
What we do
What you're dressed in.
It doesn't matter to me.
None of that matters
I just want to be with you
I want to spend time in your presence
Anywhere.
Everywhere.
If we're in a fancy restaurant
White cloths covering the tables,
Candles creating shadows
Or if we're sitting at the beach
A curved rock our seat,
Our dirty sneakers pushed against one another
I just want to spend time with you
Talking
Joking
Laughing

Kissing
Where we are,
What we do
It doesn't really matter.
The only thing that matters is that I'm doing it with you
And maybe,
Maybe I only feel that way with you
Because
Before,
Before it mattered
Before it did matter
And now it doesn't
It doesn't at all.

6.

You run your finger across my leg,
My bare leg
Underneath the table
And I jump in my seat
Dropping my fork onto my plate
Creating a loud, clattering noise.
Your eyes sparkle
And you laugh at me easily
"Everything alright?" you ask.
Your finger still traces circles across my skin with your question,
And my eyes flutter at the sensation
"Fine. Just fine," I get out.
Because I don't want you to stop.
"Are you enjoying your food?" you ask me
Your hand is still placed gently on my leg.
I nod at you
But I'm not sure I can even taste my food
With you seated beside me
Those eyes staring at me
My insides are doing flips.
And I can barely touch my food.

"I'm so curious.
I want to know everything.
Everything about you," you say.
You look at me intrigued
And I look back at you, blushing
The words you say,
They slip underneath my skin
Making my whole body tingle.
"I have a younger brother,
He's a terror,
And in middle school.
My whole life,
I've been working toward university.
My parents couldn't afford to send me,
But I was able to get scholarships."
"And this little brother who is a terror,
Are you two close?"
I smile,
Thinking about him.
Thinking about home.
"Very close."
"This is good. Family is everything."
"It is."
I agree.
"And what about you?" I ask.
"I like to draw.
To create.
To think on these questions that plague people.
From what we come.

Why we are here."
You shrug at me.
"Will you show me some of your drawings?"
You smile
Squeezing onto my thigh for a moment
Before letting go
And it sends goosebumps across my skin
"Of course I will.
I am not good,
But I will share them with you."
You take a drink of water
And all I can feel is the absence of your hand,
Your hand on my thigh
And it makes me uncomfortable
Because I want you touching me again.
"Show me tonight?" I say,
More than ask.
I'm not sure why I ask.
But I just hope that you will agree.
Your gaze flicks up to mine,
And I see a hint of a smile form on your face,
"I will show you tonight."
My body relaxes with your words
And I finally pick up my fork again.

"These drawings.
They are so emotional.
So dark."
I trace my fingers across random papers,

Stuck to your walls.

Thrown across a desk.

Packed into notebooks.

You stand in the corner of the room,

Watching me.

Watching me look through all of the things you've drawn

Feelings housed deep within you

Now scratched onto paper

Because these images

These sketches

They are raw

They are messy.

But they are real.

You nod at me.

"I was once hurt from love.

It was some time ago.

And many of my drawings,

They show how I felt at that time."

"Do you still draw those things,

Those feelings,

Now?"

You smile at me

Pushing off a wall you were leaning on.

"Now,

I draw many things.

But I am not still hurting from this past love.

I just am very unorganized."

You say the last words shyly,

Walking toward me.

"You are very good," I say,
Watching you approach me.
You wrap your fingers around my waist.
"It is something I do just for myself.
But thank you."
Your head tilts down
And you press your lips against mine,
My fingers sliding up your chest
Resting on your shoulders.
I hear a loud noise come from behind your door and pull back
"Sorry, my roommates," you whisper,
Shaking your head.
"We share this apartment together."
I nod at you,
Giggling quietly at the boasting conversation in the next room.
Your lips come down onto my forehead,
And you pull me against your chest.
Wrapping yourself around me.
And my giggles stop.
My chest is rising and falling,
Rising and falling in sync with yours.
And it takes up all of my attention
The feeling of being up against you
"Will you stay with me tonight?"
"What?" I reply,
Pulling my head back.
You laugh easily

Your presence collected
"I do not mean sleep with me.
I mean, sleep beside me.
Let me hold you.
Stay with me."
Your breath catches at your last words,
Your blue eyes reach into mine.
And before I know what I'm doing, I'm nodding
Nodding my head yes
Because I don't want to leave
I don't want to leave you.
You give me clothes to sleep in,
And then we're both in bed.
Your arms wrap around me,
And you kiss me.
You kiss my lips
Across my jaw
Down to my neck
You kiss me for a long time.
But then you turn me around,
Pulling me against your chest.
And you place your arm around my waist,
Holding me.
You hold me like that all night long.

7.

As I leave class,
With my friends walking beside me
My heart feels like it might melt
Or burst
Because there,
Standing with his side against a brick wall
Is a boy
My boy.
You.
You have on a fitted black polo that pulls across your chest
And tapered black pants that mold to your legs
I watch as you take an inhale of your cigarette,
My eyes trailing up to the fingers holding it.
All I can see is the outline of your muscles under your shirt,
Tattoos trailing down across your forearms
And every part of me thinks I've gone to heaven.
My friends turn to me,
Giving me excited eyes
Because, in your other hand, you hold flowers
A bouquet of roses.
I give a small wave to them as I walk toward you
And that is when you finally spot me

Those piercing blue eyes smile back at me.
I can't even speak when I finally get in front of you
Because you leave me speechless.
Everything about you is perfect
Those blue eyes
Thick stubble
Your perfectly fitted black polo.
But mostly the fact that you,
The most beautiful boy
You're here for me
To see me
And I think that is the part that leaves me without words.
"Hello," you smile, looking down at me through thick black lashes.
You put out your cigarette,
Pushing yourself up and off the wall.
"Hi," I whisper, leaning into you,
A shy smile on my face.
"I worked only a half day today.
I wanted to come surprise you," you say warmly,
Leaning down into me.
"I've brought you flowers."
You search my eyes before placing a kiss onto my lips.
One of those kisses where both of our eyes are open
Because sometimes,
The life playing out in front of you is better than anything you could imagine.
Imagine with closed eyes.
"They're beautiful."

You're beautiful.
It's funny to me.
How different we look.
I have on a light-purple sweater.
My hair up in a curling pony.
And then you.
You stand in front of me,
Like some god from another place.
A darker,
Smokier place.
But a perfect place.
I bury my head in your shirt
Soaking in your scent
It's a smell I've come to know instantly
Smoke and sunshine.
It floats around me
Drawing me in closer to you
Every time you embrace me
Every time I think of you
I smell that scent.
And it makes every part of my body go weak
My lips curve into a smile as I inhale
As I inhale the scent that is you.
"I will take you to get coffee?" you ask me.
I nod against you
Still folded into your body
But I open my eyes
Peeking down to your hand beside you
Still holding a bouquet of roses

Red roses

Just for me

My face blushes and I keep trying to hold back my grin

I can't help but squeeze you tighter against me

And you just laugh happily,

And I think it might be the most amazing sound I've ever
heard.

8.

Slipping my hand below your boxers is something I've never
dared to do before.
Our hands have explored
Above the buttons,
But never below.
Even though I've slept over
Stayed with you
It has always been innocent
Kisses
Conversations
Things hadn't gotten to that
I hadn't become so desperate.
But tonight,
Wrapped up in your arms
In your bed,
Everything smells like you
And our kisses aren't innocent.
We hadn't come to that point yet,
Until now
Because now your body is grinding against me
Your fingers exploring my bare stomach
Leaving burning trails

And I can't help myself
My palm moves against your stomach
And it tightens under my hand
Dipping inward, the lower I move.
My insides drop as I slip my hand into your jeans
And I'm met with the soft fabric of your underwear.
Your body stiffens
Freezing in place
Your chest rising and falling against me,
Your hands stuck to my waist.
You don't move
And neither do I
I think we're both holding our breath
Holding our breath together as my fingers dance against the
edge of your underwear.
Against our innocence
"We can stop," you breathe against me,
And I feel your body fighting itself.
"Do not feel shy to tell me. We will do what you are
comfortable with," you say,
Those blue eyes looking into mine.
I look back,
Pulling you down against my lips again.
Your stomach is hard and warm underneath my palm
My fingers graze your hip bones,
Sending shivers down through my body.
Those hip bones
Bones pointing me toward one thing
I slip my hand down further,

Scraping my fingers against you
You moan into my mouth,
And I feel my eyes rolling back at the sound.
Because feeling your soft hair under my nails makes me want
to moan too.
And a moment later, my hand finds what it has been
searching for
And it's like I've pressed the play button again
You shudder against me
Dragging your hands against my waist
Up and down my stomach
Exploring every piece of bare skin you can find
And your lips press hard into mine
Your mouth opening mine up,
Forcing yourself inside
Your tongue trails over my teeth
And mingles with my own
I feel like my body might burst
I've never seen you,
Felt you
So passionate
So intense
So out of control
And I'm the one making you feel this way
And it is going straight to my head
In the best way possible.
My hand trails back up
And I fumble with your buttons
Trying to get your whole body

Your bare body
Against mine
So you help me.
Leaning back, you slip out of your pants
All the while staring at me.
But you keep your underwear on
And all I can do is stare at you
How your stomach tightens as you move
I glimpse a hidden tattoo on your side.
But then I shift,
So my face is hovering over yours
And I kiss you
Lying there on your back
Looking completely and utterly perfect
"You're so beautiful," I whisper to you as I slip my hand
under the fabric.
I watch your face change
It becomes,
Not harsh,
But defined,
And you suck in a breath
Before pulling me down to your lips
And it's like I can feel differently now
I'm connected with you in this way
This way in which your emotions become mine
Your body syncs with mine
And your longing for me,
Becomes my longing for you.
Your hand slips back down across my belly

And your fingers play with the skin above my jeans
Tickling back and forth
But never dipping beneath
I stop kissing you
Pulling my face away from yours.
And you sit up
Moving yourself onto your side
So, now, it's you
Staring down at me.
"Do you want this?"
Your eyes search mine,
Your fingers still dancing across my belly, making it hard to
think.
But I pause for a moment,
Because there's no coming back from this.
I can already see it in your eyes.
And I can already feel it in my heart.
The moment your fingers dip below my jeans,
The moment you really touch me,
It's all over.
I'm going to be yours.
And I already know it.
"I want you to touch me," I finally speak.
You just nod at me
Your lips moving to my cheek
Trailing up to kiss my eyes
My nose.
Your lips keep moving across my face
As your fingers slip below my underwear

And the moment your fingers find my bare skin
I lose it
I lose everything in that moment.

9.

"We should go to the jungle," I sigh,
Grabbing your hand as we walk through town.
Old buildings in this seaside town jutting out at us
Cobblestone streets leading in one general direction
The Atlantic to our left.
"Just me and you."
"What would we do there?" you ask,
Wrapping your arm around my shoulders,
Pulling me against your side
"We wouldn't have to do anything.
We would be free.
Free to be what we want.
To do whatever we want."
"Do you not feel free now?" you ask.
My body is tucked against you
Trying to walk straight through the horde of people
Filling the streets on this cloudy afternoon.
"I suppose I do.
But just imagine it.
Only me and you.
Filling our time with whatever we want.
No work. No school.

No expectations."

I smile at the idea.

"You want to dance in the rain, yes?

Feel a wild passion for life?" you ask me.

I nod.

"But I think, being with you, I feel free."

"This is good then," you stop, turning and smiling at me.

I grab your face,

Pulling you down to my lips

Your scruff tickling against my soft skin.

I've never felt so free.

Yet,

So safe.

And I don't really understand it.

"How can one feel free while also feeling safe?" I ask you.

"I think that's how love is supposed to make you feel," you admit.

And I just nod,

Holding tighter around your waist.

"Maybe it is," I agree, swallowing.

You place a kiss onto my cheek as we continue walking

Walking down this cobblestone street

On a cloudy, rainy day

In the middle of summer

In a country far north of the equator.

And I wonder,

Would being in a jungle

Away from everyone

Everything

Make me feel free if you weren't there
Or would I then just feel trapped?
Trapped and alone.
Without you.

10.

I try to focus
I try not to let my mind wander
But it's becoming harder and harder
Each day I sit in class
I have to make myself listen
I have to make myself care.
My friends plan their weekends
Whispering to each other
Passing notes
They write what club they want to go to
How they are doing in their classes
Where they want to visit in the upcoming weeks we are here.
One summer.
That's all I have.
It took all of my savings to afford this summer abroad.
And I had every intention of focusing on my courses.
Getting good grades.
Having a unique experience to put on my resume.
But now.
Being here,
With you.
It's like I've stopped planning my life

And started living it.
But the problem is
It isn't something I had planned
I didn't plan to spend my nights with you
Kissing in bed
Watching old movies, so we don't really have to pay attention
Avoiding my coursework.
I didn't plan to sit at a café in the center of town
For hours on the weekend
Talking and drinking coffee with you,
You holding my hand across the table
Those blue eyes staring at me.
I need to work harder at staying focused,
On the things I wanted before I got here
But it's hard
Because every time I close my eyes
I see you.
So instead of sitting here in class
Copying notes written out on the chalkboard
I sit with my hand under my chin
Daydreaming.
About your lips
About your voice
The flowers you brought me
And your hard stomach under my hand.
I have to sit up slightly to keep my eyes from closing
Thinking about those things
And I try to stop myself
But it's hard

Because,
I'm happy.
I am so,
Extremely
Happy.
And all of my plans
All of my expectations
They vanish
Just like the notes on the chalkboard
The teacher standing with his back to us, eraser in hand.
And then, all of a sudden, I'm back
If only for a little while
Because I can't seem to wipe this crazy smile off my face.

11.

"What are your dreams. Your plans?"
"I don't have plans," you reply,
Taking a sip of coffee.
I furrow my brows
You don't have plans?
How?
I've got plans
Plans for everything
For every part of my life
"What about your dreams? What do you want from life?"
Maybe that's the better question
Maybe you'll have something more to give me
"I want to be happy," you say,
Your blue eyes never leaving mine.
"And what would make you happy?"
I take a sip of your coffee, needing something stronger than
my tea.
Your fingers slip against mine as you release the mug to me.
But then you lean back in your chair
You ponder the question
You really think about it
"I want a house."

"You want a house?" I repeat.

Finally,

That's something at least.

But I find your answer curious

"I want a house. And I want a family."

"What about a job?" I question.

A career

Doesn't that dictate our lives?

It defines who we are

Where we are able to go

The kind of people we are going to be

What type of life we can afford

But you just shrug.

"I will provide for my family, of course. But, I want for just a family.

And for my family to be happy," you smile.

And it makes me smile.

Because of everything I could want and dream,

All the different plans and goals

When it comes down to it

That is all I really want too

I want a family

A happy family

"And for you? What are your plans?" you ask me.

And instead of giving you my one

Two

And five year plan,

I just nod.

"A family sounds nice." I blush.

You take my cheek in your hand and just smile
And I feel like my heart might stop.

12.

"Will you dress me for bed tonight?" I ask.
You're seated on the corner of the bed
Your bed
Our bed
Pulling off your shoes.
We sleep in the same bed
But we don't sleep together
We just share space,
Sacred space
"Of course I can," you respond, rising from the bed,
"But I must admit, it is a unique request."
You run to my ever-overflowing duffel,
Grabbing my pink cotton short and tee set.
You love it on me
You tell me I look adorable in it
And you trace the flower pattern across it with your fingers
"No," I blurt out.
"I think, tonight, I would like to wear your shirt."
You smile warmly at me
Then that warmth seeps into a playfulness
As you strip off the shirt over your head
All I can see is your naked chest,

And my body feels on fire.
Something is moving within me
A pulse that is too fast
Too much.
You try to hand me the shirt, but I stop you
"I think you misunderstand."
My eyes fall to the floor
I'm not sure why I want this
What part of me thinks this is a good idea
Even a normal request
"Will you undress me?
All of me.
And then place me in your shirt.
Just your shirt."
I want to be wrapped in something that is just yours.
Your hand shakes slightly,
My clothes moving back and forth in your fingers
And your eyes don't leave mine
"I will do this for you, yes," you hesitate.
Your body finally moves again
Placing my pajama set onto the bed,
Perfectly stacked.
You move in front of me
Your fingers dancing against the hem of my shirt
My shirt and my stomach
Your fingers grazing my skin,
And my eyes flutter closed for a moment.
When I open them again,
You're looking directly at me

Directly at me as you pull at my shirt
Lifting it over my head
Bringing my hands back down to my sides.
I watch as you lower your hands to my jeans
Your body still held up straight.
Your muscles tense as you start at the top button
Moving one to the next.
And I can see your chest rising,
But your eyes stay focused,
Focused on the task of my buttons.
You slip my jeans over my hips
Moving them down my leg,
And I place my hands on your shoulders as you squat down,
Pulling my feet free.
I stand still,
Afraid if I move, my heart might rip out of my chest
It's beating so fast.
You stand back up
Moving to the bed
Grabbing your shirt from it.
But when you turn toward me,
I shake my head.
"You're not done yet," I say,
And I watch as you lick your lips
Because you've seen parts of me naked
But not all of me naked
Not at once
And not just standing in front of you
And I'm scared

I'm really scared
But I want this
I want this with only you.
You throw your shirt over your shoulder
Moving in front of me again,
Staring into my eyes
Pleading with me.
As your arms wrap around me,
To my back
To my bra
You unclip it,
And when you take it off of me
You move backward,
And the gaze that was locked on my eyes drops
It drops to my bare chest
And I watch, nervous for your reaction.
Your body does a sort of shudder
Your chest rising
Quickly falling, yet rising again
"Only one more thing," I barely whisper.
Your eyes slip back up my body to meet mine
And you don't say anything
You don't reply to me
You just step forward
Cautiously moving toward me
As though with one wrong step, you could crumble.
Your hands hang at your sides,
And I lightly place my fingers atop your forearms
Feeling you tremble.

Those blue eyes lock onto mine
And I have to bite my lip
To keep everything inside me from spilling out
All my emotions
All the feelings bubbling deep within my stomach.
My gaze slips from yours
Moving over the muscles of your shoulders.
But your hand rises,
Your index finger moving under my chin
Lifting my head back up so I'm forced to look at you
Forced to meet your gaze.
My cheeks flush
But I hold your eyes
And I can feel your hot breath against my face
Coming out shakily
As you move your hands to my hips,
Hooking your fingers into the sides of my underwear.
Your eyes close slowly,
Opening again.
And as they do, you breathe out,
Your shoulders moving forward as your hands slide down my
legs,
Taking my underwear with them.
I feel them fall to the floor,
And with my hands on your forearms
I step out of them,
And I move you back
So that you can look at me
Look at all of me.

All I want is to close my eyes as I do it,
But I don't.
Because this is right.
This is what I want.
"I want you to see me like this,
To know how vulnerable you make me."
Your eyes fall across all of my body
And your hand rises to touch your mouth
Your fingers gliding over your lips and down your chin
Until your hand falls back beside you.
And then with some sort of internal recognition
Your hand rises to your shirt thrown over your shoulder
And you grab at it, stepping toward me
"Wait,
I want you to kiss me," I whisper.
Your head tilts back, and I see your eyes flutter
And my eyes drift to your shorts
At the buttons keeping all of your perfect body from me.
Your lips meet mine,
Softly moving against them.
And I can feel the empty space between our bodies as though
it has its own presence.
Your hand moves around my neck,
Slipping down over my collarbone,
As your finger glides lazily over my chest and tummy.
With each inch your finger moves further down my body,
Your lips become more intense
More insistent
But I pull back as your finger rests close to my belly button

My chest rising and falling
Pounding
And my hand moves to your lips
Tracing their shape with my finger.
Your eyes reconnect with mine.
"Tonight," I breathe.
"Tonight, I want you to kiss me.
I want you to kiss me everywhere."
For a moment, there is a stillness.
As the words leave my lips, my own heart stops.
But then I feel your jaw loosen underneath my finger
And you swallow hard
Your eyes search back and forth between mine
Maybe looking for doubt
But I know they won't find any.
Your eyes stop searching, and you move your hands to my face
Cradling my cheeks in your palms.
You nod your head at me
Over and over
You just keep nodding
Before your lips finally move back onto mine.
For a moment, we stand kissing,
But then I feel your arms wrap around me
And you're moving me onto the bed
Your lips connecting with my belly
Your tongue tracing circles,
Your lips moving up and over my chest.
And taking my hand in yours,

You kiss the inside of my wrist
Those blue eyes staring into mine the whole time.
It leaves my whole body aching
Aching for you
And as your body slips down further on the bed
I close my eyes.
But it's my heart that is aching when I feel your hand on my leg.
You kiss across my hips, down my thighs, and back up again.
You kiss
Every
Single
Part of me.
And it leaves me breathless.
Completely breathless.

13.

You brought me out into nature today.
You begged me for fresh air
Needing to feel the grass underneath you
The peace of the wind
The smell of wood.
Different from the cold place you work in
Concrete always surrounding you.
So you've brought me to this tree
With your sketchbook
And sitting below it, you draw for me
Different things.
Dark things.
Easy things.
You draw a swallow.
Like the one singing in the tree above us
Like the one I found etched into your skin.
But then you draw me a heart
A locked heart
You show me how our heart can be locked up by our head
Are all of our hearts limited by our thoughts?
By our doubts. Our questions.
By logic

Does our mind get in the way of what we feel?
Or does it protect us?
Maybe if we went with what our hearts told us
We would be less confused
Less conflicted.
But that's human nature.
We don't take the easy way out
We like things messy
And complicated
Our hearts and our heads are at war.
They battle one another
And maybe, what we're searching for,
What we're all searching for
Is to find something,
Or someone,
On which our hearts and our heads can agree.
If we can find that, then we would know
We would know it is right
We would be able to feel it within our bones
Within our souls
Our heart and head could finally agree,
And we would be free
Free from doubt
And uncertainty.
As you draw these things
And talk to me
I only wish that I might be that someone to you,
The person on which your heart and head might agree.

14.

"You know what?" you smile at me,
Grabbing onto my hand as we walk down to the rocky beach.
To your favorite place
To my favorite place
I watch as your dimples pop out
Your lips curving into a smile
And I have to bite my lip,
To keep my own smile from coming out.
"What's that?" I ask.
"You're very sensitive."
"I'm what?" I laugh.
"This is a good thing. You are thoughtful. But most do not
see this softness, do they?"
"What makes you say that?" I question.
"You're strong. But I also see, sometimes, that you are
vulnerable."
"It's not like I hide it," I say a little defensively.
"But you do not openly share these things, do you?"
"I suppose I don't see a point," I state.
"I know who I am. I don't let things affect me that shouldn't.
I'm in control of how I feel.
Of my emotions."

But am I?

You reach out to me.

"It's okay to let me in," you state.

Those blue eyes pouring into mine.

"Everyone feels doubt. Fear. You can tell me the things on your heart."

Your statement isn't for you.

You aren't being selfish

You aren't trying to pry me open

You're giving me an option

You're caring about me

And it makes me scared.

"I don't enjoy those feelings."

Feeling out of control.

I push my hands through my hair,

Getting it away from my face.

"We aren't always in control, are we?" you ask.

"I'm in control of me," I reply.

"But some things are out of our hands.

Even things that are our own."

"Like what?" I ask curiously,

Walking alongside you.

"For example, the way this makes you feel," you say,

Running your finger up my arm.

You stop,

Taking my hand in yours, pulling me toward you

Against you.

Your fingers lightly move across my back,

Sending goosebumps across my skin.

"I'm not in control of this.

The way you make me feel.

And you cannot control how I make you feel either, can you?"

Your breath is warm against my cheek, and you place a kiss onto it.

Dipping your head down to my neck

You trail kisses across it

And my body trembles at your touch

You laugh warmly in my ear

"See?" you say.

"You cannot help yourself when it comes to me," you smile.

"That is called cheating," I say back to you, grinning.

You take my hand back in yours,

Walking alongside me again.

"You must know, I respect how strong you are,"

You speak hesitantly

"But it is okay too, if you aren't always so strong with me.

I see you.

I see all of you,"

You whisper the last words and squeeze my hand tighter for a moment,

Then release the pressure.

Your words settle into my chest

And I have to keep looking ahead

Looking forward

Because I can't look at you

I think if I do,

I might break down

And I can't.
I can't break down in front of you
Not yet.
Because I know all of the emotions that are waiting to
explode
I know the way I feel about you
How deeply I feel for you
And you're right
I have no control over it.
And it is the most terrifying,
Terrifying feeling.

15.

I rest my head on your chest,
Feeling your body move underneath me.
Each breath flowing through your body
A body rising and falling.
It's an addicting feeling
To lie against you
My head pressed to your chest
Listening to your heart beat
Feeling your body underneath mine.
Your finger is tracing circles against my skin
Dancing over my arm
Mindlessly moving across me.
It's as though, with each breath,
I breathe with you too.
Every inhale,
I inhale with you.
And with each of your exhales
Well,
I inhale those too.
I take in everything you have to give.
Your warm breath dances around me
And I breathe it in

Getting high off of it
Getting high off of you.
I wrap around you tighter
Your essence surrounding me,
Your warmth engulfing me,
And I feel lost in you.
But I'm fully aware of it
And I'm in control
And the best part is that I know you are in control too.
"You don't have to be here, you know," I say.
"And you don't have to lie here with me," you respond.
"But I want to," I answer.
"And I want to, too," you say, hugging me closer.
I breathe against your chest
"I'm starting to wonder something."
"Hmm?" you mumble out,
Still sliding your fingers across my skin
Leaving goosebumps in their wake
"What happens if I let you truly care for me?"
"What do you mean?" you ask.
"What happens if I open myself up to you, fully?"
I prop myself up onto my elbows.
Looking into your eyes.
Because the truth is, I am already opening myself up
I feel myself slipping away
Further and further each day
Because soon enough,
You are going to hold every part of me in your hands
Whether I want you to or not

And I want to know what to expect.

Your eyes don't leave mine,

"If you give me your heart, I will cherish it."

"But will you break it?"

You wrap your arms around me tighter,

Pulling me back down against your warm chest

A chest I feel safe tucked into.

"I couldn't break your heart," you state.

"How do you know that?" I ask.

"Because if I broke your heart, it would break my own to do so.

I don't ever want to let you go,

But if I knew it was what would make you happy,

Then I suppose I would."

"You would let me go?" I whisper.

"I would only do so if I knew it meant keeping your heart whole.

I don't ever want to hurt you."

"Aren't you scared? Of these feelings?" I question.

"Of course.

But this is life.

To not love is to not live."

"So you have these feelings for everyone then?" I ask teasingly.

You trace your finger across my lips

And you move my head up,

Your eyes looking into mine.

"I think if you let me love you fully, you will be happy.

I think I could make you happy."

You place a kiss onto my lips,
Pulling me back down against your chest.
Inhaling and exhaling.
And I think you might be right.

16.

You ash your cigarette,
And I watch it slowly fall apart.
The fire consuming it
Wearing it down
Breaking it apart
I can't help but wonder about the fire
Is it consuming that which is in its path?
Is it spreading?
Or is it slowly burning out?
Does the same thing happen with love?
Once it is lit,
Does it catch that which is in its path on fire?
Does it spread, always consuming?
Until it's consumed everything it can
Slowly dying out
Yet, if a little more is given to it
It can be kindled
It will catch aflame again
Spreading further
But it always requires something to burn
To thrive
To overtake

Is love the same?
Or is love set apart?
Will love consume?
Does love take
Or is love the opposite of fire?
Does it give?
Do you give love and receive more from that love
Or will it just consume what you give it
Until there is nothing left of you
Nothing left of either of you?
"What's on your mind?" you ask me as your cigarette goes
out,
And I can't help but tell you exactly what I'm thinking,
So I let you in.
And you just smile at me
Because even though I don't have the answer
And neither do you,
You understand.
You understand all of me.

17.

"Sometimes, I feel like I'm suffocating
I hurt so badly.
So deeply.
And I don't know how to express it.
I don't like to."
My breath catches and my chest aches at the words leaving
my lips,
But I know you need to hear them.
"What are you so afraid of?" you whisper to me.
"I don't know.
I'm afraid of letting people see me.
See me vulnerable.
Sometimes, things are fine.
Then there are other times
When my emotions hold so much power over me.
And I don't know what to do with them
They just sit inside,
Slowly consuming me."
My chest is pounding at my own words.
Because I don't like to talk about these things
I like to hide them away
But you wanted to know

Needed to know.

"You can express this pain to me. Always."

You lightly stroke my cheek with your finger.

"I don't want to," I admit.

Your gaze on me intensifies,

And it makes me want to hide within myself

"Why?" you ask,

Your brows furrowing

And I hear it in your voice

You're pleading with me

"Because these pains,

They burrow themselves so deeply that I can hardly find them.

And I don't like to think of these things,

These things that bring me pain."

You nod.

"I understand this.

There is not a point dwelling on things we cannot change."

And I nod back.

I grab onto your hand, squeezing it

My thumb rubbing back and forth across your skin.

"I think if I allow those emotions out,

If deep within me I open that box,

I'm scared it will just cause me more pain."

"But do you believe this is also how you let that pain go?"

I blink a few times at your question

"Maybe."

I think we all hold onto things

Things that, no matter how much attention or time

Will never leave us.

There are certain people, experiences,

That leave marks on our hearts forever

Good ones

And bad.

"I think," you start,

Your gaze moving from me out to the ocean,

And I feel your body slip away from me slightly

"I think what you're most afraid of is losing control.

The trouble is,

We cannot always be in control."

"Who are you to say such a thing? You don't know me,"

I respond quickly,

Angrily.

"I know this to be true because

I do know you.

And you know this to be true as well."

You try to look at me, but I won't let you

"You need to stop," I breathe out.

I can feel my body shaking slightly

And I let go of your hand,

Standing up

Because I can't sit there.

I can't catch my breath.

You're getting too close to me

And you are figuring out too much.

But you're right.

I am afraid.

Desperately afraid.

Of letting someone in completely
Of losing myself to someone
I grab at my sides,
Taking a breath.
"See,
Look at you.
You feel out of control and can barely stand it.
You have emotions in that box,
Emotions you haven't addressed.
But you pretend everything is perfect.
You pretend you're okay.
And everyone believes you.
But not me.
I see right through you."
You grab onto my hand, stroking across my fingers.
"And that's what scares you most, isn't it?
That I see past everything?"

18.

"How are your courses going?" you ask.
Your fingers are moving through my hair
Playing with a strand that's fallen over my shoulder
Your fingers sliding across my bare skin.
"I'm slightly distracted," I admit.
"You're distracted?" you question, not following.
"In my courses.
My mind keeps leaving the lecture."
Moving to other thoughts
Moving to you.
I blush
You sit up straighter, dropping the strand
"This cannot be.
You must take more care to study. I cannot be the reason
your marks fall."
I sit up too, looking you in the eyes.
"My marks aren't falling,
And I'm getting my work done."
I just keep finding it harder and harder to focus on those old
professors,
Those professors with their thick accents and rounded bellies.
"I really do try."

But my mind keeps slipping to you
I search your eyes
And I can see the concern in them
You know how important these courses are to me
And I can understand why this is upsetting to you
But I didn't say it to upset you
"Stop overthinking it," I say, dropping my finger onto your
nose for a moment,
Causing your eyes to soften.
You take my finger
Pulling it against your lips
Kissing across it,
Over my hand
And to the inside of my wrist
"So tell me then, where does your mind go?"
I blush slightly
Thinking back to all the thoughts I have when I should be
learning.
"Now, I must know," you say, grinning
Your finger pinching against my already-reddened cheek
"I think of you," I answer.
"What about me?" you smirk.
"I think about your smile," I reply,
Running my finger across your lip,
Pulling it slightly
"I think about your beautiful blue eyes.
Sometimes, my mind moves to the past.
To the things you said to me that have stuck with me."
"Is that all?" you ask, moving closer.

You start running your finger against my leg
Goosebumps forming on my skin.
I close my eyes for a moment
"Sometimes, I think about kissing you.
The way you smell.
How I think I could recognize your scent anywhere." I smile.
"Is that so?" you grin back, your lips moving to my hand
again,
Kissing against my skin
Your fingers still trailing over my exposed thighs
"Sometimes, I feel so desperate to be near you
To feel you beside me,
I like to imagine I'm that swallow
Etched into your skin.
I envy it.
Because it always gets to be near your heart
Always touching your perfect skin."
My eyes drop when the words leave my lips
Because I know I sound crazy
And the redness comes back to my cheeks.
Your fingers stop grazing my skin
And my heart drops
Because I know I've said too much.
You move your fingers under my chin
Lifting my head up
So I have to look at you
So I have to face you
You search my eyes for a moment.
"I love you,

"I love you so much."
You say those words and then close your mouth
And you close your eyes.
And then you move your lips onto mine,
Pressing them hard against my own.
I don't know if it is the blush already on my skin
Or if it is your lips against mine
Or the words you just spoke
But my whole body feels like it's floating on a swing
Going up and back down
Your hands cup my face
And I can feel your passion when you kiss me
Your lips pressing into me
Your hands holding onto me
With everything you have.
My heart aches at your words
And tears slip from my eyes
Because I'm happy.
And because I'm scared.
Those words have me feeling completely out of control
You break away from my face
Your finger coming to my cheek,
Catching a stray tear rolling its way down
"A happy tear, I hope?" you ask,
Connecting those blue eyes with mine.
I see your shoulders drop slightly, and my hands go to them
Feeling your body rise and fall under my palms.
"Very happy tears." I smile at you
And they are.

Because even though I'm desperately afraid.

I'm happy.

I'm happier than I've ever been.

19.

Lying in bed
In my own bed
I can't believe
How much I want you.
My friends wanted to have a girls' night together
We had drinks
And snacks
Watched a movie
Talked.
It was nice
But they had to beg me to stay
And I needed them to
I needed to spend time with them
To breathe in air that isn't you
But it doesn't change anything
Because lying here in bed
My body aches for you.
My blood pounds within me
At the thought of being with you.
I can't think of anything, except touching you
Touching you again
Having my lips on your skin

Your bare body pressed against mine
Into mine
Going beyond anything we've done yet.
It's not the thought of pleasure that has my head spinning
Because I already know
That my imagination won't do it justice
But my mind,
The thing my mind can't stop imagining
Is getting a part of you
Being allowed to make love to you
To show you how much I love you
How much I love you.
My blood pounds at those words forming in my head.
My insides twist,
Thinking about running my fingers down your chest
Of kissing over your collarbone,
Moving my lips to your stomach
Feeling your hips under my hands
Everything in me stills
It tightens
And for a moment, I can't breathe
Because I ache,
For you
I want to touch you
To experience you fully
You're so beautiful
And touching you, it would be like touching god
Getting to kiss and feel such a perfect creation
A creation I think was made just for me

The thought makes me feel light-headed
Like I'm floating away
But then I think of the things you might do to me
Your stubble tickling over me
It makes me grab my stomach.
My heart aches
And my chest flushes
Your body on top of me
Connected with me
In me
The thought brings a shudder through my body
And I know how much I want you
And how much I love you
I think it is time that I showed you
And I think it is time I told you
Told you how much
And how deeply
I love you.

20.

"Make love to me," I whisper,
Lying in bed with you.
Your body shifts
And you pull me onto your lap
Wrapping your arms around me
Holding me close.
With a certain amount of desperation, you look at me.
Staring into your eyes,
I breathe you in
"I will make love to you. Over and over."
I can't help but pull my eyes from yours,
A flush spreading across my cheeks
Down to my chest
"I will make love to you.
With my eyes.
With my lips.
With my body.
And with my heart."
You gaze at me, licking your lips as I lace my fingers around
your neck.
"I'm scared," I say.
"Of what?" you breathe back out at me.

Your arms closing tighter around me
"I'm scared of how you make me feel.
Of the things you say."
"Love can set you free, if you let it," you reply,
Grabbing onto my cheek, so I'm forced to look at you.
Into your blue eyes
Blue eyes that pool with desire
With love.
With a wisdom I've never experienced from anyone else.
"It also can break you."
I can't help but shake, thinking about the part of myself I'm
about to give.
Give to you.
But I want this.
I want this with you.
If anyone deserves my heart
My body
My soul
It's you.
"You don't understand," you tell me.
"You can break me too.
I'm scared too.
I love you very deeply. But this is good.
This love is the love in which you risk everything for."
"So we are both giving our hearts?" I say back.
"We both are," you agree.
And it makes me want to cry.
And kiss you.
And hold you.

"I love you," I whisper,
Holding your face in the palms of my hands this time.
I watch your eyes,
And your arms wrap tighter around me
"You love me?" you ask me.
Your voice hoarse.
"I love you," I repeat, placing my hands onto your shoulders.
Your blue eyes grow brighter as I repeat my words
And a smile comes to your face
And it brings a smile to mine.
I slip my fingers down your shoulders,
Running them across your collarbone
And I shiver at the feeling.
"And I love you," you say through your smile before pressing
your lips onto mine.
Your tongue runs against my teeth
But then you slip me off of your lap.
You move me so I'm standing.
So we're both standing.
"May I undress you again tonight?"
I don't respond
I can't say anything
I just nod my head as you move toward me.
I lift my arms, and you grab onto my shirt
Pulling it over my shoulders
Setting it onto the bed.
Then you kneel down.
On your knees.
Your fingers fumble against my buttons

You unhook them
Sliding them off.
Placing my hands on your shoulders, I step out.
Your eyes move up my body
And then you lace your fingers through mine
And kiss me.
Your lips delicately move against mine.
And then your hands move.
They slide up my arms,
Creating goosebumps across my skin
I can't help the feeling forming in the pit of my stomach
It feels as though it is dropping,
Dropping as your fingers glide over my skin
Up to my shoulders,
Sliding across the straps of my bra.
A shiver runs through me.
My heart feels like it might jump out of my chest.
"Would you like me to undress you?" I ask.
You suck your cheeks in slightly, nodding at me.
So I tug at your shirt,
And you move your arms up as I pull it over your head
There's something so intimate about undressing someone.
It's as though you're a child again
It is something you can do for yourself
But something that someone else is willing to do for you.
And it is a good feeling.
I move to your jeans, undoing the buttons, and I slowly pull
them down.
I can't help my eyes

They move across your body
Taking in your tattoos
Your tight stomach
Thin legs
Dark hair
I watch as you do the same to me
Standing back, you examine me
Examine everything I am
"You are so beautiful," you say, taking a step closer
But I move back slightly
I can't help it
I'm so nervous
Nervous about what you will think of me
Think of my body
Of how I make love
What if everything you feel about me changes tonight?
Is that even possible?
Can you be in love and make terrible love?
But as I look into your eyes, I know
I know my insecurities are unnecessary
Because you are grinning
Beaming with a bright smile
And I can't help but smile back at you.
My lips curve up, and my eyes sparkle
Matching yours
But as quickly as your grin came,
It goes
It leaves as I move my hands to my back.
To the hook on my bra.

My fingers fumble against it
But soon, it is unhooked
And it drops to the floor.
You watch as my chest becomes exposed to you
And your eyes change
They grow darker.
I watch as your lips part,
Your tongue moving to run along your lip.
And, for a moment, I wish that tongue was moving across my lips.
I make eye contact with you for a moment
But then I have to look away
As another flush moves across my skin
And I know what I need to do next.
I move my fingers to my underwear,
Slipping my finger into the sides of them
I pull them down
I pull them off
They rest at my feet, and I can't look up from the floor.
I feel so exposed
So vulnerable
But within a moment, you've moved in front of me
"Look me in the eyes," you say.
I love you
And I want to be with you
But this is the scariest thing I have ever done
"I want to show you how much I love you," you whisper in my ear,
And I melt against you

My skin flushes
And I watch,
I watch as your eyes never leave mine
I watch as you pull down your underwear
I can't move my gaze away.
You're so beautiful
Every part of you
Your body a sculpture.
Carved perfectly.
Something from heaven,
Brought down to earth,
Brought just for me.

21.

I'm trying to hold on
I'm tying to hold onto who I was before you
Of the things I wanted
All my goals
I'm trying to hold onto a single piece of myself that hasn't
been touched by you.
Changed by you.
But I'm finding it hard
Because all my goals
All the things I wanted
All the things I thought made me who I am
Don't seem as important
They aren't important if I have to give you up to get them
I still want to remain me
Keep those things that make me,
Me
But what if to be fully myself, I need you?
If I give up things I used to want for a new future
A future I could create with you
Is that wrong?
Or is that just love?
Love that makes people travel across the world

Fight wars
The type of love people give everything for
And I know one thing for sure
I would give up everything for you.

22.

"I promise," you whisper,
Wrapping your legs and arms around me
Wrapping yourself around me
"You promise what?" I smile,
Tracing over a tattoo on your shoulder
"I promise to love you forever."
You smile at me, and your dimple comes out
I stare at you
Looking into those blue eyes
Those blue eyes I told I loved last night
Those blue eyes that made love to me
I stare back at you
And then your mouth drops onto mine.
You part your lips, letting your tongue slide across mine.
I suck on you, pulling your lip between my teeth
You grab against my waist
Your fingers fumbling against my tee shirt,
Pulling it higher up my thighs,
Grabbing at my skin.
"I love you," I say, stopping to catch my breath
To catch those eyes
But then your fingers are sliding across my skin again

And I need you.
You strip off my clothes
You strip off your clothes
And we become one
Two souls become one
"I will give you everything," you whisper in my ear
As you bite against my neck
"I don't need anything. Just you."
My nails dig into your shoulders as your fingers explore my body
Your lips hot against my neck
"Every piece of me is now yours.
I am forever yours."
You say the words as you slip inside me
And I close my eyes and see stars.

23.

Sometimes, I get so lost
Lost in my own head
My thoughts
My dreams
My reality
The lines between them are getting harder to distinguish
To find.
My future
Our future
It goes beyond this summer
It goes beyond everything I once thought I wanted for myself
I dream of our future together
I dream of you
And it's getting hard to know
What's real
What's possible
And what are just hopeful thoughts within my head.

24.

I can see the beautiful garden
Growing within your head
It is always blossoming
And blooming.
I see you
Sitting there, staring at the piece of paper
Trying to create
Create something of meaning.
You rake your hands through your hair
Your eyes are tired
It's late
You sip on coffee
And I watch you
You struggle to find inspiration
Something that transcends words
But I see it
I see it within you
That you can do it
You will create something meaningful.
A garden is within your head,
Always growing
And I smile to myself

Knowing that you'll eventually figure it out too,
And find within yourself what your soul seems to be
searching for.

25.

"What do you want to do today?" you ask.
I could think of a million things
I want to do everything with you
Experience everything with you
We could stay in
Curled against one another
But I get up.
I want to do something fun
I want to see you laugh
"Why don't we go dancing tonight?" I suggest
You lean up on your elbows
Your weight shifting on the mattress
"I did not know you enjoyed dancing."
"I'm a horrible dancer,
But the thought of dancing with you gives me butterflies," I
admit.
It gives me a reason to be pressed against for you hours
To let my hands explore your body
To kiss you
It's just another excuse to do all the things I love to do to you
Your lip curves up
And I can tell you're considering it

"If you want to dance, of course I will dance with you."
"I think you just want to see me in a tight dress," I smirk.
Your eyebrows rise as you grin
"Will I be seeing you in a tight dress?"
I love how your eyes sparkle at me
They're playful
You look me over.
"You might," I reply and move next to you on the bed
The look in your eyes sends goosebumps across my body.
I kiss against your lips
Feeling your smile still on them
And it makes me smile
We both end up laughing
And smiling
Like crazy fools
Two crazy fools in love
And maybe that's what we are
Crazy
Or fools
Either way
I don't care
Because crazy or a fool
I'm happy
And I know you are too.

26.

There's something about the nighttime here.
The cool Atlantic breeze mingles with the summer air.
We need light jackets, walking to the club
And you throw your arm around my shoulders,
Tucking me against your side.
As you light a cigarette
The smoke dances in the air
Making everything slightly foggy
And it's the same type of air that is in the club.
I feel like my body is floating away
Dancing to the music.
With just a few drinks, I'm tingling
Everything is vibrating
Everything is pounding
People sway alongside us
Laughing
And singing to the music
We push through the crowd
Back to the bar
So you can get a drink.
Your arm is wrapped around me
And you look down at me,

A smile coming to your lips.
Those blue eyes of yours make my face light up
Those blue eyes.
"Hi," I whisper,
Pressing a kiss onto your lips.
You taste like the beer you just took a sip of
Like the way you tasted the first night we met
We're tucked away in a crowded place
Your scent of smoke and sunshine
Another crisp black shirt gracing your body
Everything about you tonight takes me back
To the night we first met
And you,
You take my breath away.
You finish your beer,
Dropping it onto the bar, and take my hand,
Leading me back into the center of the club.
Back to where we have been dancing together
Laughing together
Singing along
And it feels good
To let go.
But the music shifts to something slower
Deeper,
And your fingers lace themselves around my waist,
Pulling me against you
Pulling me against your chest
A chest rising up and down,
Your hard stomach pressed into mine

And my head fogs.
Because instead of feeling like I might float away
I feel desperate for you.
You press your lips onto mine,
And move them down over my jaw
To my neck
To my ear
To my chest
You kiss across my bare skin, everywhere
Standing there, swaying to the music
And every part of me wants this
Each time your lips press down onto a different piece of my skin,
It's like you're kissing me again for the first time
My heart stops with each kiss
And it has me feeling completely wild.
Completely out of control.
You lazily pull back
A smile pulling at your lips
Those thick black lashes blinking easily at me
But my eyes,
They feel like they are full of fire
You lick your lips, your fingers dancing across my back
And my body takes over
I grab onto your hand
Pulling you toward the exit of the club
"I need some air," is all I get out.
I need to breathe
I need to clear my head

Because I'm already high off of your body
And having your lips on me
Your scent surrounding me
It's too much
My body can't handle it.
There's a spot for smoking when we exit
And you grab onto your jacket
But I pull you away
I pull you around the corner
Away from people
Away from the noise
I try to collect myself
But my body is fighting me.
You take my hand in yours,
"Is everything okay?" you ask.
"Everything's okay," I breathe out, leaning my back against a
brick wall.
You can feel the music from within, trying to escape
But we're alone
Separated from everyone by a brick wall
And I've never been so grateful in my life.
My chest is still pounding
And I wrap my hands around your waist
Pulling you closer to me
Pulling your lips against mine
And I'm not soft
I grab at your shoulders
I scrape my fingers across your back
Through your hair

Grabbing onto any part of you I can
Because I need you
I get lost in your hot breath
I get lost in your lips
Your stubble tickles my face, and I laugh lightly against your
lips
My face flushed.
But then your fingers move into my hair
And the smile on my face drifts away
You bite against my neck
Leaving marks in your path
Marks that match the internal ones you've left on me.
Your body is hot against mine
And even in this cool air, my body is warm
I've never wanted you so badly before
To have you closer to me
Connected to me
Inside me.
"I want you," I beg.
"I want you now."
My fingers slip up under your shirt
And they dip below your pants,
My nails moving in circles across your skin
I can feel you stiffen against me
Stilling for a moment.
But then you press your body fully against me
Pushing me back against the wall
And your fingers slide down my sides
Across my dress

And down my hips
Your hands grazing my thighs,
And I let out a small moan at the sensation
Your hands dig into my skin, slipping under my dress
Lifting my legs around you
Pressing your body against me
And my body feels like it could burst.
I fumble with your pants,
My hands switching between your buttons
Your hair
And then running across your chest and shoulders
I can't control myself
I don't know where my fingers want to explore next
They want to be everywhere at once
Your lips are moving down across my chest again
Holding me up, pressed against you
Pressed against you and this brick wall
And the moment that your body finally connects with mine,
Everything that was holding me together falls apart
And I lose all control
I lose everything to you.

27.

"Come here," I giggle, tossing a pencil at you.
You move beside me
Wrapping your arms around my waist
Pulling me against your chest.
We're surrounded by my coursework
By textbooks
All spread out across your room
It's a rainy Sunday afternoon,
Giving me a chance to catch up on reading
Get ahead in my assignments.
You move your finger across my lips,
Lightly touching the tip of my nose with the pencil I threw at you
Your eyes sparkling.
"One day, I will take you to my home," you tell me.
"And what will we do there?" I ask.
"We will visit my family. We could live there one day, if you'd like."
"That's your dream, isn't it?
To one day be with your family again?"
You nod at me
"Yes. And to be with you," you respond.

"I think that is a good dream."
"I will take you to visit one day. To the old towns.
The forest.
The sea.
I think you would enjoy Montenegro."
I agree with you
I would love it
I *will* love it
But I would love anywhere,
As long as I was with you.
Your fingers slip across my back and up into my hair
Playing with a strand
"Just imagine, one day, we could be sunbathing on the
beaches of the Adriatic."
I can imagine it
I can imagine you there
Standing beneath the sunlight
Looking like a god
"Not stuck inside because of the never-ending rain," I add
lightly.
You nod your head at me,
Moving your fingers to tickle against my sides.
"I promise,
One day, I will take you there."
And you smile brightly at me.
And I smile brightly back at you.

28.

Grass stains on our clothes,
Your hands are tangled in my hair.
The air smells of moist dew
And your body lies atop mine
Moving against me
Moving within me.
And I grab onto you
A layer of dew covering your skin,
Our bodies dancing together under the warming sun.
I pull you closer
And lace my fingers around your waist.
Moving my hips,
My legs stick against yours
And I feel you becoming breathless.
The clouds move above us
And I watch them
Surrounding you
Surrounding us
In a divine warmth
In the early morning light
Feeling as full as one person can.
Your hand slips across my skin

Sliding over my collarbone and down my waist
Pulling my dress higher
I can feel dew starting to cover every part of me
Every part of you
Where your hair meets your neck
Where your stomach presses against mine
Love and warmth.
It is all I feel
And all I can see.
Your fingers dig into the grass around me
And I press my hips into you.
You shudder at the motion
Shaking against me
And then your body pushes into mine
Your head falling against my chest.
You wrap around me,
Pushing me down into the soft dew-covered grass
And I lay my head back
Smiling up at the clouds
Radiating.

29.

"I will always happily lie here with you."
"Of course you would. I'm naked now," I tease.
"I don't see it like that," you reply.
"What do you mean?"
"Yes, you're naked,
But what I mean to say is, I see you vulnerable like this.
You don't just strip off your clothes to me now.
You strip away everything else
So I can see your heart."
Your words sink into me
And I think only you
Could make two people lying in bed naked together
Sound so beautiful
So enlightening
So profound.
"I think you might be vulnerable here then too," I agree.
Because you're right
I am vulnerable
Vulnerable with you.
"You do?"
Your blue eyes look surprised
Your hands move against my belly,

Tracing dancing circles across it
I nod
"The way you look at me.
The way you love me.
With so much passion and heart.
I think it makes you extraordinary."
"But you think it makes me vulnerable?"
I just nod.
"I think it does."
You love with so much.
You give me so much of yourself
It means you have everything to lose
Just like me.
"I don't want to lose you," you say seriously,
Your fingers dropping onto my skin
The circles on my belly ceasing.
"You will never lose me," I reply, squeezing your hand
And I bring your lips up to mine for a moment.
You drop your head back down onto my chest,
Your fingers dancing across my skin again.
"Do you think" you start,
But your voice cuts off
And I feel you shaking your head against me.
"Do I think what?" I ask.
Your fingers slip across my arm,
Down to my hand and against my fingers
"Could you see us married one day?"
My heart leaps
And you have to hear it

Feel it
Pounding in my chest
But you stay lazily on top of me
Still playing with my fingers
"Could you imagine it?" you ask.
You slightly lift your head up slightly,
Pressing your lips into my skin
The skin of my exposed chest
And then rest your chin on me
Those blue eyes gazing into mine.
"I could imagine it."
I nod over and over
You smile at me
And nod back
Dropping your head back down onto my chest.
Looking up at the ceiling,
With your body resting against mine
I can more than imagine it.

30.

The more you tell me about your family back home,
The more you tell me about your mother,
About your grandmother,
About your siblings,
The more I can't help but fall in love with them too
They raised you to be the person you are now
They helped you figure out who you would become
You tell me about your family
About the people who raised you
About childhood memories
And about growing up
How you got to where you are now
How you got to me
A smile always on your face,
Your eyes lighting up
And it makes my heart so full.
Love created you.
The divine manifested you into being.
Nature helped you grow into the person you are today
And so I sit here,
Silently thanking every one of them
For bringing you to me

Because
Without you
I couldn't be me
I wouldn't be complete.
Not anymore.

31.

The idea of just touching you
Makes my stomach drop
I want to scrape my fingers against your skin
Over your shoulders and down your arms
Running my fingertips along the tattoos I've stared at so
many times.
Your stomach dips in
Slightly jutting back out at your hips
Then tapering in just below
I look over you
And I can't breathe
Because I'm in love with your body
Because I'm in love with you
I look into your blue eyes
And my stomach slips down further
I need you
I want you
I want to touch you, so I do.
I can't help myself.
You lick your lips
And I have to bite my own from moving my mouth to yours
To taking your tongue

That tongue
Within my own mouth.
I trace my fingers across your arms
Over your tattoos
Down your side
My fingers falling onto a swallow etched into you.
Goosebumps rise on your skin.
I watch your eyes as they darken
And your chest moves up and down
It heaves and catches as I move my fingers against your skin
My own eyes darken at the sensation
At the feeling of your want for me
I slip my fingers down your chest
Against your stomach
Tracing the line above your underwear.
And your eyes leave mine.
I watch as you stare at my lips
As you look at them with such longing
You grab onto my face
Pulling me to your lips
Against your chest
Grabbing onto me like you have nothing left
Like I'm everything to you
Like you're everything to me.

32.

There is something in the air at night
Everything is still
There is silence
The busy day slips away
The ache of life lifting off
Sometimes, at night
In the pure blackness that engulfs your room
In the time between dream and reality
I talk
"I'm so afraid."
"I'm afraid of so many things."
"I'm afraid of disappointing my family."
"I'm afraid of the choices we are going to have to make."
"I'm afraid of losing you."
"And I'm afraid of losing myself completely to you."
As I speak,
You never move
You don't come closer to me,
Slipping your fingers against my skin
You leave me where I am in bed beside you,
Alone in the darkness
You stay perfectly still

"Fear is okay,
But in the end, it does no good.
And one thing you should know is that you are enough.
And you will never lose me."
I tell you all these things
And it feels like I'm talking to myself
Like I've created the conversation in my head
Because I can't see you
Feel you
But I hear you
I hear your words
And, sometimes, you hear me cry
Because it is that time between day and night
Light and dark
Dream and reality
My mind gives in to my emotions, and I let them out
I give them to you
Just like you wanted
In the darkness, you get a glimpse of the pain held within me
But when we wake
I have a smile on my face
Because it's day again
Reality is back
And everything is as it should be
I never let my fears follow me into the light
And you never ask about them unless we are alone in the
darkness
And I love you so much for that
Because you understand me
You understand me completely.

33.

Lying on the couch
I need you.
I need to be closer to you
I make you slip into me
I don't need you to make love to me
I don't need you to move
I just need you
I need you to fill me
I need you to make me feel full
With your body pressed into mine
I've never been so comfortable,
So content
So in the moment
But I've never felt so dependent
Dependent upon someone else.
I need you to feel complete
To function
To feel normal
And I'm starting to wonder,
To what extent do I need you
Do I need you to be just me?
To be myself

Are you a part of myself
Or am I becoming someone mixed with you?
Needing you
Always needing you
And if I'm always needing you
Needing you beside me
In me
Is that a good thing?

34.

"What do you think?" I ask
Smiling at the environment surrounding us.
We are seated on a quilt
Picnic basket placed beside my leg
Wine and treats coming out of it.
You brought me here once before
To this place
This castle
Consumed in time
Overcome by vines
You brought me to this place where time stood still.
You grab at my legs
Playing with the hem of my dress
I let out a giggle
I want to run away from you
I want you to chase me
To have my chest heaving
As you catch me
And kiss me
Pressing me up against this abandoned castle
This castle full of history
Of past secrets

Of past love
But I don't want to run
I don't want to wait
Your hand slips further up my leg
Under my dress
And my breath catches
It catches in the way it would have had you chased me
Caught me.
Because you've already caught me
And I can't move
My body feels stuck
Still within the moment
Building with pleasure and emotion
Your lips move onto mine
And your hand moves against me.
I kiss your shoulder,
Pulling you closer to me
On top of me
I need you on me
Your skin touching mine.
You move your fingers back down my leg
And I shiver under you
And that is all it takes
For me to lose control
Your fingers on me
Your fingers in me
Your heart in my own
I lay my head back onto the quilt
Chasing the sun, hidden behind the ever-present clouds

And I can't help but smile up at the clouds
At the sky
At the sun
At you
Your gaze stays connected with mine
Your face hovering above me
And everything within me warms
Because you are my sun
You are the thing that brightens my day
You're my everything
And I giggle as you look down at me
My hair spread out across the grass
Your body resting on top of mine
You grin at me
And I grin back
Because we're living in a moment of bliss
That we've created just for ourselves
Consumed by love.

35.

"I think, one day, you're going to make me the happiest man in the world."
"One day?" I ask.
"What about now?"
"I'm quite content, yes," you admit.
"But, one day, we will get married.
I will be the most happiest then."
Your gaze isn't on me
It isn't on anything in particular
Seated outside one of the restaurants in town,
We sit, talking
"Will that be the day?" I smile.
"Up until then, yes," you agree.
And I can see your mind working behind those eyes
"And then, one day, you will give me a child.
And our child will be the most extraordinary thing I will have
ever set my eyes on,
Apart from you."
My whole body is glowing at your words
Glowing in love
"You want to be surrounded by babies one day, don't you?"
You just grin at me

"Our babies, yes."

"And what makes you think I'll give you these things?" I tease.

Your eyes fill with amusement

But then become serious again

"I know in my heart you will.

We will do these things together.

Experience them as one."

"I think we will too." I flush.

Hearing you speak about our future

The things you want from life

From me

It makes my heart full

"This life isn't meant for you and me to go through alone now.

Now, I believe it is a life we are supposed to share as one."

For someone so young

Your words are profound

And your determination sends a shiver down my spine

Not because I'm scared

I'm not scared anymore

But because everything I could have ever wanted

I have

I have you.

"Going through life with a common breath?"

You nod

"You'll make me the happiest man because of these things.

It's the little things, you know

The little things end up being the biggest things,

The moments we will cherish."
"The glances we remember,
The laughter we share," I add.
I understand what you mean.
"The events of our life will be remembered through moments,
And I think we will have all of these moments together."
The words leave your lips,
And your gaze finally connects with mine
You don't say these things looking for the right response from me.
You say them because they are the words kept in your heart
And you are sharing that heart with me
"I think you might be right."

36.

You're the thread
The single golden thread that holds my universe together
Without you,
Everything falls apart
It all disconnects
But with you there,
It fits
It all fits
Who I am
What I love
Who I want to be
What I want from life
You make it all feel possible
You make it possible
Everything I am and could be works with you,
Is because of you
You hold my life together
The single golden thread
Woven through my universe
Woven into my universe
Holding it all together.

37.

"Will you say my name?"
"What?" I breathe against your cheek,
My lips lightly moving across your skin
Placing hot kisses across your jaw
Over your stubble
Onto your soft cheek
In the middle of the night
In the middle of your room
In this perfect bed of yours
"I want you to tell me all the things you've told me so many
times before.
But say them,
Addressing me."
Your blue eyes move up to meet my gaze
"Am I missing something?" I whisper to you
"I just want to hear it,
I mean to say, I *need* to hear it,
My name coming from those lips of yours."
You trace over my bottom lip
Your finger slightly pulling at it as it slips down and over
But your eyes slip away from mine
And I know you're having a hard time

You're struggling today
And I can see that
Because I leave in a week
And we haven't talked about it yet
I can't talk about it
Every time I think of leaving, I feel like I'm breaking apart
"I want to hear all the things you think and feel for me," you reply.
Your eyes coming back up to mine,
Your face serious.
Your head rests in the crook of your arm,
And I move one of my hands to your face
Running my fingers across the stubble
And I move my lips to meet yours
Pressing into you with everything I have
And you kiss me back.
"…, I love you."
"…, I love it when you're inside me."
"…, you make me feel whole."
"…, you make everything okay."
I kiss across your face,
My lips landing on your nose
Moving up to your forehead,
And I run my fingers through your hair.
I whisper words into your ear
The way you make me feel
How much I love you.
You lie there with your eyes shut for a while
And I can see the pain on your face

"…, I will never hurt you. Of all the things in this world I'm sure about,
Knowing I will never hurt you is one of them."
Your grab onto me
Your fingers pressing into me
And, when I look into your eyes, they're pooling
Pooling with pain
With sadness.
You wrap me up,
Tucking me into your body
And all I can feel is you shaking against me
And then I feel my shoulder get wet
Wet from the tears slipping down your cheeks
And onto my skin
All I can do is hold you tighter
And whisper over and over,
"I love you."
But, now, I'm crying too
And I feel helpless.

38.

"I don't want to lose you," I whisper.
Back at the beach
That rocky beach that is your favorite place
The hard waves crashing against the shore
The ocean showing me its pain
Its anger
"You won't. Why would you think this?" you look at me,
concerned.
"Last night—" I start,
But you stand up.
"I thought the fears we shared at night didn't follow us into
the morning?"
Your words are harsh.
And true.
"I know you,
And me not being here,
We haven't talked about it.
That I'm leaving."
You're pacing in front of me
Kicking rocks on the beach
Pebbles flying one at a time in different directions
"You want to be with me still, yes?"

Your question is simple
And my answer is simple
"Yes."
You nod your head at me.
"I don't want to go," I say desperately.
"But I have to.
School is starting up again,
And I've got scholarships.
It's the only way I am able to go.
I can't lose that."
"I know you must go,
But do not doubt my love.
We will make it work,
We will be together again.
I know this to be true."
I nod my head, standing up in front of you
Grabbing at your hands
Running my fingers across your skin
Up your arms
"I love you."
I pull you to my lips
Feeling the breeze whipping at my face
The coolness chills me
But your lips are warm
And reassuring
And when I pull back
Your blue eyes sparkle at me
And it makes me feel okay
But I know you,

And to cope with not being together,
I don't know how you will handle it.
You love so deeply
It's your biggest strength
And deepest weakness
Because it can destroy you
Love can destroy you
And I just hope you don't get scared
Because if you do
You'll destroy me too.

39.

"I will be your reason," you say.
"Please, look at me," I beg,
Because I hear the sadness in your voice.
Your eyes pooling with tears
You turn your head away from me
"I live for everyone else.
I care for my family so much
I care for you so much
But I cannot be with them.
I cannot be with you.
And it isn't fair."
My breath catches at your words.
"No, it's not."
"But," you say, wiping at your eyes
Swollen and red
"I can always be your reason."
You take my hand in yours
"My reason?"
"Your reason," you nod.
"When you are in so much pain you cannot think straight,
I hope you get through it for me.
When you feel lost, find your way out for me.

When your heart feels hardened, soften it again for me.
Do it because you know I'm here for you
Because you know I love you.
Even if you are strong on your own
Know that you always have me
And I will be your strength
When you need a little extra
Whatever you think you can't handle,
Can't accomplish,
Know I believe in you
I will be your reason
For getting through
For becoming who you are meant to become
I can at least take pride in that."
I don't know how you formed these thoughts
These words.
But you say them with tears in your eyes
And it breaks my heart.
"Promise me?"
Your eyes are pleading.
And my insides drop.
"I promise.
I promise you will always be my reason."
You nod your head,
Wiping away at your tears
And I pull you against me
Pushing your head against my chest
Running my fingers through your hair.
"Thank you.

This, this gives me purpose.

And I need this now."

And I know you do.

I have one more week.

We have one week.

And I think you feel the same way I feel about it.

Completely helpless.

40.

"I can't go. I love you."
My heart breaks, saying the words
"You must."
Your hands are shaking.
Holding onto my face,
You press your palms against me
Squeezing my cheeks.
Your eyes are red
And they look hollow.
Those bright eyes I love
They're red and empty
And it hurts
It hurts me deep within my stomach
Because you need me
You need me as much as I need you
But you're right
I have to go.
People pass by us
My friends wait patiently at the gate
They don't understand anything
They don't understand what this means to me
What you mean to me

And what I mean to you
They think it is just a fling
A romance
That I'll write you into my journal as an experience
A fun summer romance
But they couldn't be further from the truth.
Tears sting against my skin
My nose raw.
You stand, holding me
Pressing me against your body.
You can't move either.
My arms are wrapped around yours
My fingers sliding against your back
Over the muscles I've felt under my hands a hundred times
I know your body better than anyone
"I love you so much," you whisper into my ear.
"We will be together again soon, over the holidays."
I nod
Try to pull myself together
For your sake
And mine
"You're right."
I try to give you a small smile.
You squeeze my hands
Holding them up to your lips
And kiss against my knuckles
"Call me once you arrive home?"
You ask the question,
And tears slip from my eyes

Because you're saying goodbye
And I have to say goodbye
"I will."
You nod your head at me
And then you kiss my hands hard,
Pulling me to your lips
And I taste your tears on them
My tears on them
But then you step back
And that's it
I have to turn away
I have to walk to the plane
But you're looking at me
Like you have nothing left to give
Like you're defeated
Like your heart aches
Like your body aches
And it makes my stomach drop
It twists within me
And I want to scream at the sensation.
Seeing you in so much pain
It makes me hurt
I see you suffering
And I feel even more pain because of it
Seeing you this way destroys me
It breaks my heart
It breaks my heart, watching yours break
Tears stain your cheeks
But you give me a small smile

And a little wave
And even that tears me apart
I watch you
Breaking in front of me
And all I can do is run back to you
Kissing you one more time
Whispering against your lips
How much I love you.

41.

Even though I'm coming home
I feel like a stranger
A stranger to my life
A stranger to this place
To what I once knew
To what I once used to be
Because this trip changed me
Love changed me
You changed me
You took a piece of me
And I'm coming back without it
To a life I love
To a family I love
Knowing that everything is different
Knowing that I am different
Everything around me has stayed the same
But my heart will never go back to the way it was before you
And I never want it to
But now I have to figure out where I fit
Where I fit in the life I left three months ago
And am returning to.
Where do I go from here?

And how do you fit into this world?
Can two separate people
In two separate places
Create a life together
While not being together
Not knowing what the future holds,
Or how our dreams will become a reality
And is love
Our love,
Going to be enough?

42.

It's been one month
One month since coming home
And things are okay
School has been busy
And I talk to you all the time
You call me
Send me photos
Random messages
It's not perfect
It's not our forever
But I think it's enough for now
And I think we can make it work
I really think we can.

43.

You send me a photo
You're hunched over
A wide smile on your face
It's blurred slightly
But raw
Authentic
Real
It makes my insides twist.
Even seeing you through a screen,
My body has a physical response
Goosebumps climb my legs
My stomach tightens at the sensation
And I can't help the shiver that runs through me
The lump that forms in my throat
My body buzzes
It buzzes for you.
It's the best feeling in the world
Knowing that you're thinking of me
I look at your eyes
Those blue eyes
And even a thousand miles away
It feels as though you're right in front of me
Smiling across the room at me for the first time.

44.

"You are so beautiful."
Your messages fill my head
They consume my thoughts.
You tell me you think about me
You think of being with me
Kissing me.
I think about being with you
"I wish you were here."
"What would you do if I were?" I reply,
Butterflies forming in my stomach
"I would kiss you. Over and over. I would never stop."
"You will be here in a few months, and then you can."
I smile down at my phone
"And it will be as if no time has passed," you say back.
Just a few more months
Until you'll be here,
Standing in front of me.
You've asked for time off,
You're saving for a flight.
"I love you," I say.
"I love you," you reply.

45.

"I miss you," you say,
Your voice coming through on my phone
It takes my breath away
Hearing your voice.
Sometimes at night, I call you
I don't want to talk
I just want to listen to you breathing
I pretend you're lying next to me
Holding me
My head rising up and down on your chest
With every heartbeat
"I miss you," I respond.
You talk to me about how work is going
What your friends are doing
What book you're reading
And I tell you about my family
About school
It's funny to think back,
Back to my time with you
One look
One kiss
One conversation

And that's all it took
My fate was sealed.
I like to think that love
True love
Doesn't know time
It doesn't know distance
Love isn't simple
Our love isn't simple
But it's love
And it's you
And I will always love you.

46.

"Can you hear me?"
Your words come through over the phone
And I have to grab at my stomach,
Hearing your voice
"I can hear you."
Just your voice over the phone
Sends shivers down my arms.
Each time I hear your voice
I'm taken back to a moment
A moment in which we were together
And the memories have my head spinning
"I do not know how else to say this,
But I cannot visit you."
At first, I think you're joking
Because you're supposed to be here,
With me,
In a week
"What? Why?"
I hear you sigh
"I have to change my flight.
I must go to Montenegro.
My grandmother is ill.

Very ill,
And I must go to my family."
My heart is pounding against my chest
And everything within me starts to ache
"I...,
I don't know what to say.
I'm so sorry."
"This is how it must be."
Your voice sounds heavy,
And defeated
Over the phone
And it makes my stomach twist
"So then, I won't be seeing you next week."
But I already know the answer
It is no
I'm not going to see you
After talking on the phone for months.
After dreaming of this time together.
And I want to scream,
To tell you that you have to come
To tell you to forget about your family
I want to be selfish
But I don't say anything
"I have no control over this," you whisper into the phone.
"We are being torn apart.
This hurts me too.
But it is my family.
I don't have a choice."
And you don't.

I know you don't.
Because, if you did,
I know you would be here.
You would be with me.
"I know. I just—
I just feel so broken."
A shudder rushes through my body
And I start crying over the phone
Crying into the phone
I feel broken
Now what do we have to look forward to?
I listen to you breathe
Breathing over the phone
And your breaths becoming shaky
And we are both crying
Silently into the phone
Silently to each other.
"I do not know how we will continue to make this work."
Your words ring in my ears
And everything feels heavy around me
But my body feels light
And it is a strange feeling
A horrible feeling
"What are you saying?"
Tears slip down my face,
And I bite my lip to keep from crying out.
I hear you breathe out another sigh.
"I love you,
But I am hurting.

I am hurting you.
I wanted to see you, and I do not know what to do now.
I'm sorry."
I wish I could see you,
Hold you in my arms.
But your voice,
It is all I have of you now.
We're prisoners to the distance.
"We will figure something out.
I could try to visit over spring break."
I don't know what else to say.
Except we have to make something work.
We have to figure it out
Because I need to see you
I need you.
We need to be together again.
"This could work," you reply to me in a shaken voice.
You sound defeated
Unsure
And I really don't like it.

47.

"Why are you doing this to me?" I ask desperately.
"I do not know what to say.
You live there.
And I'm here," you reply.
Your calls have become less and less
Since you had to go home for the holiday break.
You used to message me
Throughout the day
With random thoughts
Little notes
Now I barely get anything
With no reason.
"You told me you loved me.
That you wanted to see me.
That we would make this work."
I hear you breathing on the other end of the call.
You didn't have a choice
You had to go home
But that doesn't mean we're just done
"I told you,
I can visit in a few months,
For my spring break," I plead.

"And then what?" you ask calmly
But your words are harsh.
"And then what?! I don't know." I laugh out, defeated.
And then we'll live happily ever after.
"And then we'll figure it out," I say.
But you're right.
And then what?
I leave.
Again.
With my heart more broken.
And yours.
Broken too.
"This is hurting us too much," you whisper into the phone.
And my stomach drops.
Tears slip from my eyes.
After summer,
I left.
But we were consumed in our love
You had something to hold onto
For months, I could feel your lips on mine
Your smell on my shirts
I still feel it now,
When I think of you
But maybe you've forgotten
"But we love each other," I plead.
I hear you crying into the phone,
And I think my heart shatters
Shatters in this moment
Listening to you cry

"Please don't cry."
I ask this of you
While crying myself
Holding onto my chest
Because my whole body aches
"This longing,
For something I can't have,
This longing for you,
It's bringing me too much pain,
And I can't handle it."
Your voice is shaky
And then the call drops.
I call you back
Over and over
But you don't answer
So I sit in my room
Curled in my bed
Slowly dying.

48.

"Falling for you
That was my mistake
It was my fault
I should have never opened up to you," I say.
"You do not mean the things you say," you whisper over the
phone.
"You're wrong.
I knew that you could break my heart
I gave you everything
And it wasn't enough."
"We cannot continue to fool ourselves
It is hurting us both too much."
Those are your words
But they're wrong
You're hurting me.
"I would rather hurt,
Hurt knowing you loved me
Than hurt because you didn't."
"You know I love you," you plead with me.
"I will never stop loving you.
But you are there.
Your family.

Your life.
And I am here.
I cannot give you everything being here.
And these difference always will remain."
I can't believe your words
"So everything we shared
Our secrets,
Our dreams,
Being together one day,
None of it matters now?"
My words are harsh
And I want them to be
I want you to feel bad
I want you to give in
I want you to forget you're feeling this way
"I don't know what to say."
Those are your only words
And it's too much
"I know you can't be here,
And I can't be there yet
But, one day, I can be,
And we can be together."
I plead with you,
My voice angry
Desperate
I can hear you shaking your head
"I need some time," you breathe into the phone.
Your breath
Your words

Suck the air out of me.

"So you're saying we can't even talk?" I ask frantically.

I'm crying again

And I don't want to be

I wanted you to see my anger

Not my pain

"I cannot get past this pain if we continue to talk every day.

Being apart,

I know, though you won't admit it,

It is breaking you.

I can tell it is.

And I won't do that to you."

"Don't do this to me," I beg.

"You're just scared."

My chest is heaving

And my eyes feel like they might explode

A lump forms in my throat

Making me feel like I can't breathe

"I'm trying to spare us more pain," you say shakily.

"I do not want to continue hurting you."

"I'm not giving up on you,

I'm not giving up on us," I reply.

"Please, don't make this harder on me,

Harder than it already is," you beg.

And at those words

I can't take it

I hang up

And I scream.

49.

It's been days since we've talked
Days since you answered my calls
My messages
But today
Today, you give in
You answer my call like nothing's wrong
Like you're doing fine
And it kills me
But I let it
I put up with the pain
Just so I can hear your voice.
You answer my call,
And I think it means you're giving in
We both are going through hell
Putting ourselves through hell
But at least I get a small piece of you today
To know that I'm not alone
To know you haven't forgotten me
I know you care,
And that this is killing you
It has to be
So I find comfort knowing that

I'm not the only one slowly dying on the inside.
"Why—
Why did you kiss me that night?"
It's the only question I want the answer to
"If you were going to rip my heart out,
Why even bother?"
"I cannot say why exactly. I just knew I had to."
"You have no explanation?"
I need a reason
I need to know why you're hurting me
"It was out of my control."
Your voice is sad
It's defeated
And it makes me feel sick
"Out of your control? You kissed me."
"I had no choice in the matter," you plead with me.
"From the moment I saw you,
I knew,
I knew I had to kiss you."
Your answer is honest
And it makes everything worse
It makes me want to scream
I stood there, at the airport
And I saw you
I saw you break down in front of me
I saw you helpless
But I was helpless
And now
Now I feel myself breaking down in that way again

"Right."
That is the only word I can manage
You don't ask me how I am
You don't console me
You don't cry
You just say,
"I cannot answer again.
You understand this?"
Your words are raw
And I can't bear them.

50.

Looks speak louder than words
And after seeing you look at me that night
The night we first met
The night that changed my life
I should have known
I should have known then that you would love me like no one
else had
Like no one else could
That the kiss we shared would shift everything
I should have known that look
And I should have known that you would destroy me.

51.

I wake up screaming almost every night
Feeling crushed
Weighed down by sorrow
The sorrow that doesn't allow me to sleep.
I scream in my dreams
It has become my normal
My brother has gotten used to it
My parents sleep through it
I wake covered in sweat
Thinking of every dream
I dream memories,
I have nightmares
But the worst nightmare that haunts me is just of you
It's as though even knowing my fears,
You still come after me
You still find ways to hurt me in my dreams
And when I wake up covered in sweat,
Covered in tears,
I feel another piece of me break
Slowly dying a little each night.

52.

Emotions are all I seem to find
Coursing inside me
It's like I'm swimming in them
Drowning in them
And I can't escape
They're stuck within me, never leaving.
I try to get them out.
I scream
And laugh
Until I cry
But they never go away
Sometimes they change
Hurt.
Anger.
Pain.
Dread.
Hopelessness.
They are all my demons
They are all drowning me
But one is the worst
One attacks me,
Over and over,

Never letting up,
Never letting me go.
Fear.
Fear that you will never love me like you used to
Fear that you won't realize you've made a mistake
Fear that you could see me as just someone from your past
Fear that you might try to find it with someone else
That is what always sends me over the edge
The thought of you with someone else
I can't breathe when I think about it.
I try
But it doesn't do any good
Because as long as you are not with me
I will never make it out of these emotions,
I am stuck, always drowning in them.

53.

My mom took me to a doctor today
She's always looking at me concerned
But I'm not sure why
She knows what happened between us
She knows how you destroyed me
I couldn't tell her at first
I thought you would come back to me
I thought you would change your mind
But you didn't
And I started having nightmares
I started having anxiety
I started screaming in my dreams.
The doctor looks at me
Looks at my chart
"You've lost weight."
Those are his only words to me.
And I'm not surprised
I haven't eaten much
I can't eat anything.
With everything I do
My stomach aches
My insides are constantly falling through the air

Nothing to catch me at the bottom
So I continue falling.
I'm not sure if I will ever stop feeling this way
If my insides will ever finally hit the ground
And it's a terrible feeling.

54.

You torment me.
You haunt my dreams.
I see you next to me in bed
Pressing up against me
Your warm body next to mine.
Wrapping your arms around me,
You pull me onto you.
And I smile.
You always make me smile.
You kiss me, moving my hair to the side.
My curls tumbling over my shoulder,
Your lips trailing across my neck.
Even fully clothed, I feel naked.
Naked against your skin.
My thoughts, naked to you too.
I've told you all my secrets.
Given them to you
You know everything
My hopes.
My desires.
My demons.
You tug me closer, and I find comfort.

I find warmth.
I find love.
But then I wake up.
And I realize that the love I just experienced,
Was only a dream.
And I have to continue on
Go about my day as though it hasn't already been shaken
As though I haven't been moved within my core.
I live through the trauma
The trauma of loving you in my dreams.

55.

I've gone numb
I can think about you now
And feel nothing
I can think about anything
And feel nothing
I sit in class
Staring at the teacher
I sit at the dinner table
Staring at my food
I sit in my room
Watching my mother pace in front of me, concerned
I sit at the doctor's
Watching him look from my chart to me
I still do these things
I still move
But my face
My whole body
Feels numb
And I think I would rather feel this emptiness
Than the pain I felt before.

56.

It's been nine months and five days since we met
Nine months and five days of love
Of pain
Of agony
It's been nine months and five days
Since you first kissed me
It's been eight months and fifteen days since you first told me
you loved me
It's been eight months and ten days since we made love for
the first time
Nine months and five days ago you made me question
everything
My whole world changed that day
You changed me that day.
And I think I hate you for it
Because *you* have caused me this agony
You've caused me this pain
It's been nine months and five days since the worst and best
day of my life
I wish nine months and five days ago we'd never met
That you'd never kissed me.
I used to believe true love was real

I used to believe that love could conquer everything
But if you've taught me anything in nine months and five
days,
It's that true love doesn't exist
Love will rip you apart
Piece by piece
And it isn't worth it
Love is selfish
And I think your love was selfish
I think *you* are selfish
I could have given you everything
I tried to give you everything
But it wasn't enough
Because it never could have been
Because I was trying to give you something that didn't
actually exist
I wish, nine months and five days ago, you had never been at
that bar
That you hadn't kissed me
That I hadn't fallen in love with you
That you hadn't made love to me
Making promises you couldn't keep
Promises I believed
Promises you broke
You broke my heart nine months and five days ago
Because you were selfish
And I hate you for that
I hate you.

57.

That beautiful swallow
Painted into your skin
I used to wish that I was that swallow
To have the honor of always being close to you
Now I see it in the sky
In my dreams
And it feels like it's circling me
Placing me in a cage
A cage I can't escape
When I see it,
All I can see is you
All I can feel is your body
Hear your words
Feel your lips against mine
Your chest under my hand
And my heart breaks
Because I used to think that being a swallow would be the
most beautiful thing in the world
Because I could always be with you
Near you
But now,
That swallow

It's trapped me
Placing me in this cage that I can't escape
Always haunting me
Circling me
You've placed me in this cage
Just a tiny swallow in a cage
A cage that is destroying me.

58.

I see you in my dreams still,
As much as I see you in reality.
It's getting hard to distinguish what's real
And what isn't
What are memories.
What are dreams.
And what are figments of my imagination.
You whisper words into my ear
Your fingers dancing across my shoulder
Pulling me back against your chest
Your stubble tickling my neck.
It was only a dream.
But when I wake, it's as though you are here
In my thoughts
In my reality
I can still smell you on my pillow
Feel the leftover heat of your lips on my skin
I remember the words you whispered to me
The photos you showed me
The stories and secrets you shared with me
I remember them as clearly as a cherished memory
But it was only a dream
Wasn't it?

59.

I write letters to you
On lonely nights
I think about what I should say
With pen and paper, I sit and stare
Stare at the blank page
I think about it often
How I wanted to write our story
Write out our love.
Put into words,
On paper,
How much I love you.
But I don't think words could ever do it justice
Because you can't express our hearts through language
That's where the gap lies
It's how a look can say a thousand words
But a word can only convey one
Some nights, I try to write out how I first felt when you kissed
me.
How I felt when you made love to me
The moment I knew I was in love with you
I try to write it into words
I try to understand it

But my words never make sense
They are bits and pieces of the story
Little parts that describe what I was feeling
What I saw that day
The smell in the air.
They are the movements of your body
How your lips curve over your teeth when you smile
All these things make up those moments
And I can never get them right.
But there are other nights
Nights when I write because I'm in so much pain
And I tell you how much you hurt me
I tell you about the pain
What my heart was screaming in those moments.
I write that you wrecked my life
And how ironic it is
That your biggest fear was falling in love
But you did
And I did
And so to save yourself from the pain, you left
Leaving me in pieces
I write to you all the time
Maybe one day you'll read them
But I pray you don't
Because if you knew how much I loved you
Really knew,
You would get scared,
And then you would leave me all over again.

60.

I finally feel like I'm over you
I finally feel the weight lift from my chest
But then I look
I look at old photos
I look at old messages
To see if I can handle it
To see if I'm over you
And I'm not
I laugh to myself
Hysterically
With pain.
And heartache.
Because I thought I was over you
I thought I could look
And see that it didn't affect me
To see that I would realize you were a jerk
A liar
But you weren't
You aren't
And I'm not over it
Not at all
My laughter turns to tears

And they're just as uncontrollable
I feel crazy
And so I keep laughing
And crying
Because if I'm crazy, then what does it matter?
It doesn't matter how I look
Or what I feel.
Because I've cracked.
So I laugh
And cry
And I decide I'm not crazy
I was just crazy to think I could ever get over you.

61.

Sometimes I remember a conversation we had
A word choice you used
A phrase you said
My heart swells at the memory
I hear your voice in my head
Saying those words to me
And a smile comes to my face
But then I remember,
I remember that we don't talk anymore
That I won't hear you say those things to me again
That I might never hear your voice again
And I want to break
If only I could forget those conversations
Forget you
I wish I could
I wish I could pull you out from within me.
Untangle you from around my heart.
But it's not that simple.
You're not just wrapped around it
You're in it.
And you're in me.
And I think you always will be.

I'll be walking down the street when all of a sudden,
You're there
In a smell
A familiar voice
An outline moving in front of me.
You will always be with me
Not just in my past,
But always haunting my present.

62.

The doctor tells me I've lost my faith
My faith in love
In life
In myself
He tells me I have to get it back on my own
But I've come to realize something
Many things actually
The most important being that I was too attached to you
And I can never do that again
I can't look back on my memories with emotions
I can't look upon anything with emotions
Because it will just destroy me
Our memories
They happened
They aren't going to change
I can't change my future
It's already decided
You've decided you can't be a part of it
That we aren't meant to be
That we are soul mates plagued by circumstances
By our responsibilities
By our families

We're doomed to this endless pain
And that is our fate
And since you've accepted it
Then so should I
Because if you've given up on me
Why shouldn't I give up on myself too?

63.

I imagine you here, next to me
Your warm breath on my ear
I lean into you,
Your shoulder brushes with mine
Even in this crowded room, my attention is on you
You move next to me
We aren't looking at one another
But we might as well be.
All I can feel is you against my skin.
Your words flood my ears
Your scent intoxicates me
I'm asked a question, and my gaze flickers back
Back to now
Standing alone in this room
This room filled with people
But I'm alone
Alone because I don't have you
So I pretend.
I pretend you're here with me
I pretend you're at my side
I pretend your blue eyes connect with mine
Even as we talk with others

Your presence is everywhere
I take comfort in it,
Even if I am just imagining it.
Because,
I can imagine it.
I imagine a lot of things.
It's normal to.
Isn't it?
I see you everywhere
I want to see you everywhere
Because I want you beside me
I want to share these moments with you
Like we talked about
Like we planned
If we shared these moments,
I wonder what you would say.
Perhaps the crowd is too loud
Maybe you love the song playing
You're bored
Or hungry
You think I look beautiful
Well,
I think you look beautiful too.

64.

Maybe it's better this way
Not speaking to you,
Talking to you
Because I can imagine your words
I can imagine your thoughts
I create in my head what we're doing
The words you're whispering to me
The thoughts moving in your head
The thoughts in my head
I create a story in my head
Of what I wish my life were like now,
With you in it,
If we were together.
And maybe it's better this way
Because I'm in control
I'm creating these perfect moments.
They don't actually exist.
But I just tell myself that.
It wouldn't have to be a perfect moment
Because if you were there,
Really there,
It would be better than anything I could imagine.

65.

"Sweetie, this isn't healthy."
That's all my mom says.
She sits at the foot of my bed.
Watching me.
Watching me wither away to nothing.
And I know she's right.
But it's out of my control.
"I can't change anything, Mom."
I don't have an answer for her.
I don't have any words to console her
To ease her worry.
Her brow creases,
And lines form around her eyes.
"You're going to have to."
That's her reply.
She sits at the end of my bed for a while,
Patting my legs through the comforter.
She sits there,
Watching me,
Rubbing my legs,
But then she gets up without saying anything,
And leaves.

Leaving me alone again.
Alone with my nightmares.
Alone with you.

66.

Lying awake in bed at night has become my reality.
Even awake, I see you everywhere.
But it is worse when I close my eyes.
As they flutter shut and darkness surrounds me, you come
alive.
We sleep in separate beds.
In separate countries.
On different continents.
Yet I still find you in my room each night.
You are so far from me, I should be able to forget
Forget how you smell like sunlight and smoke
How your eyes looking down at me twisted my insides
around
How your teeth left marks across my neck as you sucked and
pulled against my skin
I have space
I have distance
I have the chance to forget all those things
But I can't.
So when I close my eyes, the distance is gone.
And instead of being alone in bed, I lie with you.
I've never felt so happy

You take me into your arms and brush my hair away from my face
"I promise."
"You promise what?" I smile, running my hand down over your collarbone.
"I promise to love you forever."
You smile, and your dimple comes out
I can't help but stare at you
Your mouth drops down onto mine,
And you part your lips, letting your tongue slide into my mouth.
I pull your lip between my teeth,
And you grab my waist.
Your hands wrap around my clothing, pulling my nightgown higher up my legs
"I love you too," I say, stopping to catch my breath.
To catch your eyes
You look straight at me
Not through me
Into me
Into everything I am.
And in your gaze, I'm met with the cosmos.
And everything fades away
My purpose is clear,
And it is you
To love you.
I'm blinded by a beautiful soul staring back at me
A soul
I wrap my arms around your waist, pulling you closer

You strip off my clothes, and we become one.

Two souls become one.

"I will give you everything," you say, lying on top of me.

"I don't need anything. Just you," I reply, looking into those blue eyes.

Those blue eyes that took my heart

Those eyes I love

And they look back at me the same.

"I mean to say, I'll give you all of me.

You have me.

My body. My heart. My soul.

I'm yours.

I'm forever yours."

You say the words as you slide into me.

I close my eyes and see stars

See the stars that are within both of us

That link us

Love can conquer all things

Or so I thought.

I open my eyes as tears slip down the corners

I cradle myself in bed, pulling my legs up to my chest

Trying to comfort myself.

But I can't.

I can't breathe

Because every time I close my eyes, I see you.

I feel you

I see us

And it destroys me.

It destroys me because I don't make up what I see

This happened.
Those promises.
They were real
But they weren't true.
I claw at my chest trying to breathe
And I lie here, heaving.
Alone.

67.

Sometimes I think about you
And it makes me happy
Every part of me lights up
Warmth spreads through my stomach
Goosebumps across my skin
I think about your voice
I look at old photos
I find so much joy
I think about how happy we will be
About our future
Every photo takes me back
To a time and place where you were
A time you were thinking of only me
And I grin
I can't help the smile that comes to my lips
But then I get to the end of the photos
And it's been months since I've gotten one
Months since we've talked
And reality comes crashing back down
I try to remember the joy in those moments
To feel grateful for it
But once the love and longing passes

I'm left in darkness
Trying to fill a hole
That only you fit into
Maybe I'm just crazy
Trying to remember the love in the moments we shared
Or maybe I've just lost it
More so
Lost myself
And I think I have,
I've lost myself to you.

68.

Sometimes it's easier if I tell myself you died
I know it's wrong.
I pretend you've gone on,
But stuck around to see me,
To be with me
Because you're like a shadow, always on my shoulder.
You smile down at me
Telling me it's alright
To continue on.
You walk beside me,
Invisible to everyone else
So I tell myself that you're real.
That you're a ghost.
Not ready to move on
Not ready to leave me
I see you so clearly
That sometimes it scares me
It scares me how you come to me
Whispering words.
Sometimes I catch myself laughing
Laughing at the things you say to me
But the truth is

You're just a figment of my imagination
And I'm not sure which is worse
The fact that I tell myself you died
Or the fact that I see you everywhere.
You brush your fingers against my skin,
And I try to shake you off,
I try to get away from you.
But I can't.
And that must mean that I've really lost my mind.

69.

I know I'm losing my mind.
It's an easy thing to tell.
Most people will probably tell you they didn't realize it was
happening
That they thought they were normal
But not me
I know it's happening
And I know there is nothing I can do about it
It's actually quite comical
Watching everyone's concerned faces
They sit in front of me
Talking to me,
Like I might crack at their words.
Like if they touch me, I might shatter.
They talk to one another
In hushed voices, like I'm not in the room
Like I can't hear them
So I let them think I don't
They look so concerned
Acting frightened for me
I have to keep my lips closed to keep from laughing at them
Because,

Really,
This whole thing is hilarious.

70.

Darkness feels like it's consuming me,
It's as though it's going to swallow me whole
And I'll never be able to find my way out,
My way back.
I shut my eyes
Trying to let go of the pain.
It can only hurt me if I let it
And I try so hard not to let it hurt me
But sometimes it does
It eats at me
The weight of the world presses down on me
And I stand stuck
Stuck with this weight pounding on me.
I only wish I could fall to the ground,
Give out under the pressure of it,
At least it would be an end to the pain
But that would be too easy.
Instead I stand stuck
Frozen
With nowhere to go
And nothing to do.
But then I think of you

And it's as though the weight shifts
It's still there,
Surrounding me,
But it doesn't touch me.
It engulfs me,
But doesn't destroy me.
You don't take away the weight of the world
But you make it bearable
And that's why without you I'm stuck in a hell with no end
Nowhere to go
Nothing I can do
But wait for you to come back to me
And make everything okay.

71.

"Everything is fucking with my head."
"Excuse me?" my mom's eyes go wide.
"You heard me!
I go to school and am bored.
I go to a job that I couldn't give a shit about.
I go to a doctor who doesn't understand anything.
I can't move on.
Even if I tried.
I'm not okay.
Don't you understand that?
I'm not okay!"
Tears slip down your cheeks.
I don't like to see you cry
Not because I feel bad for you
But because it means you feel bad for me.
You are hurting for me.
And I don't want anyone suffering because of me.
I'm suffering enough.
I don't need the guilt of causing anyone else pain.
"Stop crying!" I scream.
I feel so much anger.
Rage

Heartache

Brokenness

You're putting this on me too.

Your sadness

Your disappointment

"Sweetie," you say, grabbing onto me.

"I love you, and I'm crying because when you hurt,

I hurt too."

"Well, stop! I don't need you making me feel worse."

I want to pull my hair out.

This is why I can't talk to you.

But,

This is what you don't understand.

More than anyone, seeing *you* cry,

Seeing *you* uncomfortable,

It gets underneath my skin,

It burrows within me

And dies there.

A part of me dies, seeing you this way,

Because of me.

And it makes me feel almost guilty enough to fix myself.

If only I could fix myself.

"Tell me what I can do," you cry shakily.

"All I want is to help you.

Let me help you."

You pull yourself together.

You dab away your tears.

And I see your face change.

You're being strong for me

And I know how hard it is for you,
Because emotions flow through you like I've never witnessed
in another person before.
You pull yourself together, for me.
You're strong, for me.
And it makes me want to be strong too.
And I think that might just be enough.
I want to be better,
Get better,
For you.
Because I see how much I'm hurting you.
And if I'm not strong enough to pull myself together,
For myself
Then maybe,
Maybe, I can do it for you.
Maybe.

72.

A beautiful swallow
Was etched into your body
And now it is stuck in my mind
Wherever I go
If you were to look behind my gaze
Into my mind
You would find that swallow
Flitting about,
Teasing me
Reminding me
It brings me joy,
And it brings me pain
If you looked behind my gaze
You would find your body
That beautiful swallow always in my thoughts
Your body always on my mind
You,
Always on my mind.

73.

I feel so much shame
Because I need you
I need you to get myself to that place
To that place that goes beyond everything we know
To a place of pureness
To a place where I can let go
And I can't help but feel disgusted
Disgusted with myself
That I think of you
That I have to think of you to get there
As my body shakes,
My finger moving against myself,
Tears slip from my eyes
Because this isn't right
It isn't right at all.
But it's all I have.

74.

When I think of you,
It's almost like I'm looking back
Back into a memory
A memory clouded and dense
I try to push past the thickness
The dense fog that surrounds the memories
That surrounds the memory of you
But the truth is
I don't ever want to get past it
To go back to those moments
Moments of pure joy
Of happiness
Shared only with you
The fog provides padding
Protection
From the emotions those memories hold,
The precious essence of what life is truly about.
Sometimes I push past it
Peeking back into my memories
My mind dwelling on you
On us
And I remember the love

The passion
And then all I feel is pain
Pain that rips through me
Starting at my skin,
Moving deeper and deeper until it's squeezing my heart and
stomach
Compressing and twisting so much I can't breathe
I try not to dwell on those memories.
I try not to let the emotions flow through me like
uncontrollable waves
But every now and then
I have to open the box
The box that holds you within it
So I know that even if I feel just pain
At least I can feel something
Anything
Other than numbness.

75.

I'm flipping through my textbook
Trying to speed up time
Until I'm out of this class.
I've been doing better
My family thinks so
I'm eating more
I feel better
I try to stay focused
To put my energy into something
I keep my mind on school
I'm working on a group project now
The teacher lets us play music lightly while we talk
He thinks it will help us relax
That it will let us feel as though we're out with friends
And not sitting in this humid classroom
But it's nice
It does help
It keeps my mind occupied
Someone next to me speaks
And I look up.
It's one of the girls in my group
I try to listen to her, but a new song comes on

Our song comes on
And my face goes white
I try to stay calm
I try to brush it off
I think about yelling
Yelling that they have to turn it off
Because I can't take it
But I don't
I sit
Pretending
That it doesn't affect me
That it doesn't break me in two
But tears slip down my cheeks
And I hunch over
Grabbing at my stomach
I can't breathe
I try to suck in air
But it doesn't seem to work
The girl next to me jumps up
She's standing in front of me
Her eyes frantic
And I understand that feeling
Because my whole body feels the way her eyes look.
Frantic
Lost
Confused
Aching
My head is spinning endlessly
My insides twist

I can't cope with the pain
It's consuming me
It's consuming all of me.
My whole body feels it
And it's as though it's caving in on itself
Flattening me down
Breaking me in half
I grab onto the side of the desk
Trying to pull air into my body
And everything goes fuzzy
But someone touches my back
Actually, they touch my hair
And everyone backs away
They grab at me
Pulling me against them
Against a flat chest
Stroking my hair
And I know it's you
I finally get a breath in
And my heart feels like it might burst
I can finally breathe
I lean into you
Against you
My head falling back
Resting against you
You keep stroking my hair
I squeeze my eyes closed
Sucking in air, my chest heaving
My breathing finally steadies

And I open my eyes.

People surround me

A slight distance between us

But they just stare at me

With frightened wide eyes

I turn slightly

Looking up to catch a glance of your face

But when I look up

It isn't you holding me

It's someone I don't know

A random boy in my class

My face flushes, and my eyes go wide

He is squatting down beside me

My body folded against him

Grabbing onto my hand

"Everything's alright," he breathes out,

"I think you just had a panic attack."

My eyes go wide

And then I drop his gaze

But I try to stay calm

He senses my distress

Moving closer to my ear

"My sister gets them a lot. Holding her is the only thing that can calm her down."

He stands back up

"Want me to walk you down to get some water?" he asks

I nod my head yes

Grabbing onto my bag.

I can't come back here

After that
My face is hot
My body aches
He walks next to me as I leave the room
His arm supporting me
"Thank you," I say.
I don't know what else to say.
"No worries," he replies.
We get to the water fountain
I take a sip
And splash some of it on my face
"Can I do anything else?" he asks.
His eyes seem to swim with pity
And it makes my stomach drop
But I also feel lucky
Someone was there to make the pain go away
Even for a moment
"No," I reply.
"I think I just need rest—
School stress and everything."
He nods
Understanding
But it's a lie
I grab my bag
Heading to my car
As he heads back to class
Maybe I just need some rest.
I tell myself that
Maybe it will make a difference

But no matter what I do
Where I am
Or what I try to do to occupy my mind
You're always on it
You will always be in my heart
Forever destroying it.

76.

I've never believed that doctors know anything about our minds.
They don't understand what goes on in our heads,
What goes on in our hearts
The emotions that flow from there
That form there
How thoughts come about
How they disappear
And how they change
Doctors label things
Name things
They give them a perfect description,
And then it's done
They've gained control
They think they're in control of something because they've identified it.
But if they truly understood anything about the mind
The heart
Our feelings
Then they wouldn't do such an absurd thing
They tell you there are stages
They try to get you back in control

By putting you on a fixed chart
Moving along at their predetermined pace.
Our hearts
Our heads
They aren't things that can be understood through a
prescription
Through a diagnosis
From a chart
There can't be expectations
About how people should show pain,
How people should heal.
Maybe if we weren't so afraid
So afraid of our own emotions
Of this raging ocean inside of us
We might actually be able to let it out
To face it
To let it flow freely,
Then truly be free from it
Not having ignored it
Not having closed it.
We could see these things coming,
Accept them,
And let them pass by with a smile
Thinking about these things brings me some peace
But it also tears at me
Because I sound like you
Debating our heads versus our hearts
It's something I think you would agree with
And I don't know how I feel about that yet.

77.

"I'm Mike," he says.
His hair is chestnut colored,
And he's wearing a button down.
His smile is white,
And he's cute.
I blush slightly.
It's been a while since I blushed
At the thought of someone else.
He leans into me
His lips tasting like mint
Then he slinks his arm around me
Pulling me closer after a moment
But I pull back
I can't do this
I push off of the bar
Running out the door
He tastes like mint
His hair is too light,
His eyes empty.
There's nothing,
Nothing below those eyes.

I press my fingers to my lips.
My hand is shaking.
I ruined them
I ruined my lips with his mouth.
The last lips on mine were yours
Now they are his
And I can't handle it.
I feel empty
I feel nauseous
I tried.
I tried to have fun.
I went out.
I listened to my friends
I flirted with who they told me to
And it was the worst decision
I let someone else tell me how I should feel
How I should get over you
But what they don't understand is, I'm not getting over you
There's no getting over you
Your eyes are engraved in my soul
Your lips…
Each time I close my eyes,
They're still on mine
And they always will be
It doesn't matter who else touches my lips
It won't matter
It won't change anything
Because they're not yours
So I lie in bed

And I cry
I grab onto the sheets
Shaking them
Ripping at them
I feel hollow.
Empty.
Tears stain my cheeks
And so I close my eyes
I can't help it
I can't help what I always do
What I do to cope
What I do to get through
I close my eyes
And I think of you.
You're next to me,
Your blue eyes
Your scent of smoke and sunshine
You lie with me.
And you wipe away my tears
Your lips go back onto mine
And they wash away the kiss
The kiss that ruined my lips
You make it better
You always make it better
And I fall asleep against you
Your chest rising and falling,
A smile on my face
A smile on yours.

78.

I'm scared
I'm so scared
I'm scared I'll never find someone like you again
Someone who understands me
Understands me completely
What if I do find love?
Someone who loves me
But they don't get me
Not in the way that you did
Not in the way that I want.
I want that understanding.
That love and acceptance.
That look in their eyes
That look in your eyes
You knew me from the moment you met me
Inside and out
You understood me on a level no one else had.
I'm not scared of losing you
Of having lost you.
Because what we had was special
It was beautiful
What I'm scared of is never finding it again

Of comparing everyone to you
Because they will all fall short.
They don't understand
And they never will
Because even I don't understand
But you do
You understand
You understand me.
Or at least, you did.

79.

"One day I'm going to get a rose tattoo," I whisper.
"A rose?" you smile.
"A rose," I reply,
Pulling your face closer to mine
So I can look into your eyes
So I can feel your scruff under my fingers.
You brought me my first bouquet of roses.
"They represent love and passion," I say while lightly kissing
against your lips,
Moving across to your cheek.
"All things I feel for you." I grin
Smiling against you.
Your fingers brush over my back
"Is this so?" you say,
And I can feel your smile against my own skin
"This is so. Every time I see a rose,
I will think of you," I say, promising.
Those words haunt me
Being pulled from my memory
Because here I am
Almost eleven months later
Passing a flower stand

A little cart on the side of the street
An innocent cart full of flowers
Flowers that should bring joy
And my body just stops
My feet won't move me
And my hand goes toward a bin
A bin filled with flowers I need to walk away from
But I don't.
I pick up a rose
Daring to bring it to my nose.
Inhaling its perfume,
My eyes flutter shut
And my body is back in that moment
Kissing your cheek
Both smiling wildly against the other
Wildly in love
And then my body shakes
The rose moving back and forth in my unsteady hand
My throat constricts
And it makes a noise
I make a noise
A noise that sounds like that of an animal
A dying animal
An animal in so much pain
It's muffled against my closed lips
I open my eyes
My hand moving to cover my mouth
My whole body aching
I see the woman behind the flower cart, staring at me

Her eyes drooping
While her arms hang at her sides, helpless
I know that look
It's pity
It's sadness
It's not knowing what to do or how to fix anything
A tear slips down my cheek
I forcefully wipe it away
Not wanting her to look at me like that anymore
I drop the rose back into the bin
And my insides drop with it.
I thought I was getting through this
I thought I was finally getting over you
But I didn't expect this
This reaction
This feeling
This ache in my chest, this pounding throughout my body
I didn't expect any of this.

80.

Sometimes I wonder why, after a year, I can't move past you
Why I think back to your body pressed against mine
Your warm breath on my lips
I wonder why I do it to myself
Why I can't seem to move past you
Am I holding onto a dream because I have nothing else?
Or am I meant to carry you with me?
Because you will be with me again one day.
And like the stars in heaven
We will be placed in exactly the right spot,
At the right time,
To be with one another.
Maybe it's fate.
Maybe we're fated for one another
Or maybe I'm just lonely.

81.

I keep trying
I try so hard
My friends introduced me to someone new
And we click
We can talk for hours
And he's funny
And kind
Sweet
And he likes me
And I like him
I can see myself with him
Our life could be easy
There wouldn't be heartbreak
Or anger
Confusion
And despair
In every way, he would make a good match for me
And I think life would be kind to us
I think I could be happy
But is that all I want?
To just be happy?
It's what I should want

I should want something easy
Something that comes natural
Something normal
But therein lies the problem
I don't want normal
I want you
And if that means uncertainty, then I want it
If that means fully giving my heart again,
Then I want it
If that means feeling scared that my heart could be ripped
out again,
Then I want it
Because if I gave you my heart again,
You would have to give me yours back.
Yes,
I could care for this man
I could be happy
But I will never,
Never feel the way for him that I felt,
Still feel,
For you
And therein lies my problem.

82.

I've come to realize that maybe they were right
My family
My mom
Even my doctor
Maybe everyone was right
I was too attached to you
Too dependent upon you
I loved you
I love you
But love shouldn't strangle you
It shouldn't destroy you
And I think our love,
Being apart,
It was destroying you
Love shouldn't make you ache with pain so deeply that you
think you're dying
Love should lift you
And I should have lifted you
I was selfish when you told me you couldn't handle long
distance
When you told me it hurt you too much
I loved you

But I was scared
I was afraid to lose you
I was worried about myself
It was all about me
And not you.
Love
Pure love,
Should put the other person first.
I let my fear overpower everything
And I should have realized
That to truly show you I loved you
I should have let you go.
Because I didn't want to see you in pain
Because I was causing your pain
And at the time
I wanted to
I wanted you to hurt
I wanted you to ache just as badly as me
I wanted you to feel empty
And that was wrong.

83.

I seem to be asking everyone the same question
In different ways
Should love be hard?
Should it be consuming?
Maybe it should be
Or maybe love should be easy
It should be comfortable
I get many answers
But one thing everyone seems to agree upon
Consuming love fades
It disappears as quickly as it came about
And what you're left with is everything else
You're left with a person.
You're left with conversations
Daily life
Laughing together
Crying together
You're left with normal events and small actions that make
up your day
You're not left with a consuming lustfulness
You're not left with only blinding passion
You're left with a person,

A person who is a normal.
A person who makes mistakes.
A person who messes up.
And you have to love that person
Respect that person
Because when the blinding passion is gone,
That is who you are left with.
Even though I felt that blinding passion,
Even though I felt so much hate toward you,
Even though I felt so much love toward you,
At the end of the day,
When I was there,
And we were together
I was happy.
I was happy just being with you
This normal person,
Who was extraordinary to me.

84.

"I need to go."
Four words
Just four words strung together in a sentence
A sentence created from a thought
A thought that's been on my mind for weeks now.
Those four words finally coming off of my lips
Spoken to my mom.
"Need to go where?" she asks.
You're sitting at your desk
Shifting through papers
And typing on your computer.
"I need to go back to him."
My heart pounds against my chest
Your fingers stop moving
And you look up at me
Your eyes growing wide.
"Have you two spoken?"
I shake my head.
"No.
But I'm going to tell him.
I'm transferring schools.
Next fall, I will be enrolled full-time there."

Your hand comes up to your lips
And you cover your mouth for a moment
Your fingers finally drop back down.
"You sound like you've already made your decision."
I see hurt in your eyes
"Mom,
I have to.
I love him.
I still love him.
And this life.
Here.
It's not my life without him in it.
Not anymore."
You search my eyes,
And I see your mind working.
Thoughts spinning.
"And what if things don't work out? Then what?
Will you come back home?
Are you willing to put your future on the line
For someone who has already broken your heart once?"
"Yes."
My answer is immediate.
"If things don't work out.
It's okay.
I'll be okay.
But at least I will have tried.
At least I will have done everything I could to make it work.
I love him, Mom.
And that's all there is to it."

I watch a tear slip down your cheek
And you grab my hands,
Holding them in yours.
"You went through a lot because of him.
I've never seen you so broken.
And it's scary for me,
To let you go back to someone
Who caused you that much pain."
I nod.
Because it's true.
I was a mess.
A broken mess that you had to put back together.
"I know that.
But I've changed.
I've learned from all of this.
And I'm willing to move.
I'm willing to switch schools.
I will find a new job when I'm there.
But I need to be there."
You nod at me,
Your hand pulling away from mine,
Wiping at another tear rolling down your cheek.
"If this is what you truly want,
Then I think you should go.
And I'm proud of you.
For making this decision.
For yourself."
You smile, patting away the tears.
And it makes me smile

Because, finally,
I feel proud of myself too.

85.

I think I've realized that I love you now without needing it
back
Love shouldn't require anything
It shouldn't ask for anything in return
It doesn't have conditions
It should be given freely and openly
Because,
You do have a choice
A choice to love without being loved
To give without receiving
That is the test
Of pure love
To give it without expecting it in return
Love with conditions isn't love
Love with anger and hate isn't love
I think that when I loved you before
It was selfish love
It was young love
I loved you, expecting it in return
And when I stopped getting it back
My *love*
Turned to hate

To anger
To heartbreak
I do want you to love me the way I love you
And
I still think you do
But it doesn't change the way I love you
I will love you with the same amount of passion regardless.
And at night
Before I fall asleep
I think of you,
I send you my love
I ask that you are happy
Regardless of how you feel for me.
Love can change your whole world.
And I know that you,
You've changed mine.
I loved you desperately
Selfishly
But I've changed
My love has changed.

86.

I get out my phone
And I open a new message
A new message to you
I'm going to be in Dublin in two weeks.
I want you to know,
That I fought for you.
I love you,
I still love you.
And I want all of you.
You still have my heart,
And I hope I still have yours.
If you come into Dublin,
If you come into the city,
If you show up,
We will make it work.
Together.
And if you don't,
Know that you are missing out.
Because I will love you with more passion than you could have ever
dreamed of.
And I think you already know this.

So,
This is it.
It's up to you.
I know you're scared.
But I'm scared too.
I hope to see you soon.
Always yours.

I don't tell you that I'm transferring schools.

I don't tell you that I'm moving to the small seaside town you call home.

I just tell you where I'm going to be.

Where I'm flying into.

Because I need to know if you'll show up.

Not knowing that it will be easy,

Not knowing that we will be in the same town.

Because either way,

I'm staying.

And I need to know

Will you buy a train ticket into the city

Will you show up

Will you fight for me?

87.

Saying goodbye to my family.
To my mom.
It's hard.
But it's finally time.
It's time for me to board my flight
It's time for me to go back to Ireland
Back to the country that changed everything for me
Back to the place where a single kiss shifted my whole world
And I'm nervous
I'm nervous about what will happen
I'm nervous you won't be there
I'm nervous I've made the wrong decision
But then I think about how much I still love you
And my nerves settle themselves a little
Because even nervous,
I know this is right.

88.

I asked you to meet me in Dublin,
In this random square.
There's a garden
And benches
And I couldn't think of where else to ask you to meet me
I didn't want it to be at a café.
I didn't want it to be at a restaurant
I needed somewhere with fresh air
With light
And so now
I sit here waiting
Waiting on one of the many benches in this park
To find out if my heart is going to be broken all over again.
My stomach is folding in on itself
And my whole body is shaking
And waiting.
Waiting to see if you come.

89.

I've thought a lot about seeing you again
I thought I might see you again
And not feel the same
I thought I might see you again
And my heart wouldn't break
I thought I might see you again
And my chest wouldn't burst
I thought I might see you again and things would be normal.
That the time might have changed things.
I thought a lot of things.
But the moment I see you.
I fall apart.

90.

All I can see is the blurred outline of you
Walking
Running toward me
Your eyes are pooling with tears
Matching mine
And I finally feel like I can breathe again
You wrap your arms around me
Picking me up off the ground
And you're shaking
Shaking in my arms.
"I'm sorry.
I'm so sorry.
I should have never let you go,"
You cry the words into my hair
Holding me up against you.
My cheeks are wet
And my heart feels broken into pieces
Seeing you,
Seeing you cry like this
Again
It kills me.
"Don't ever do that to me again.

You didn't just break my heart.
You broke me.
You broke me completely."
The words leave my lips
And you nod your head at me
Over and over, nodding
My whole body falling into you.
Your scent,
Smoke and sunshine,
Consumes me again.
I haven't felt you,
Heard you speak to me in person,
In a year
And nothing has changed
Nothing at all.
You pull back,
Your hands cupping my cheeks
And you look at me with those blue eyes,
Eyes that hold all of the Atlantic in them
The eyes I fell in love with.
And my fingers move to your cheek
Catching a rolling tear on my finger
It feels so good to be touching you again
Touching your face
That stubble tickling my skin.
"I am sorry for what I did.
I could hear it in your voice
I was breaking your heart by not coming to visit.
And it was horrible.

I felt helpless.
I thought if I left you alone, if I didn't keep hurting you,
It would be better.
But I was wrong."
Your voice is shaky,
But your words soak into my skin
Moving into my core
And settling there.
I nod.
"I know."
I take your hand.
"That is why I came back,
Because I know you.
And I still love you."
Your lips press onto mine
Your fingers slip around my waist
Making me feel like I can't breathe again.
My whole body is in shock at your touch,
Your hot lips against mine.
Your tongue moving against my lips, opening up my mouth.
And it feels exactly the same
It feels perfect
But you pull back.
"I have thought of many things these past months," you say,
"And I've realized I need you.
I need to be wherever you are.
So I applied and got a work visa.
So we can be together in the States."
Your words make my heart stop.

Your gaze lands on mine,
And there is a slight blush on your face
A blush I've only seen a few times before.
"You would move.
Leave everything behind
For me?" I say.
My hands are shaking slightly,
So I grab onto yours,
Lacing my fingers through them.
"Yes."
I search your eyes,
Looking for a hint of doubt.
Uncertainty.
But I don't find any.
And so I smile.
Wiping away at my tears,
Wiping away at yours.
"I love you," you whisper to me.
"And I do not know where we will live,
Where I will work.
I do not have these answers.
But the one thing I know is," you say the words,
And slowly drop down onto one knee
Still holding my hands
"I love you.
And I want to be yours.
Will you agree to marry me?"
You look up at me,
Speaking these words

And slowly drop my hands.
Reaching into your pocket, you pull out a thin,
Golden band
It's simple
And perfect.
My insides spin
Spin watching you kneeling in front of me
Here in the middle of this park
But it's right.
I put my hands on your cheeks
Your stubble thick under my fingers.
"I will marry you.
Of course I will marry you."
You stand up next to me, pulling me against you.
And you kiss me,
But then we're both crying again.
Crying and smiling.
Crying and smiling and kissing.
And as you kiss me, I can feel the smile stay on your face the
entire time.

91.

I tell you about how I got through being without you
How I didn't really get through
How much I suffered
What I went through
And you tell me about your pain.
Your suffering.
Because we both suffered
In so many ways
We both suffered.
I tell you that I transferred schools
That we can stay in Ireland
In this small town along the Atlantic
That it would make me happy
And that makes you happy
I tell you about all the things I have come to realize
About my love for you
"The way I loved you
It wasn't healthy
It was consuming
All consuming
You took up every part of my mind
And every part of my soul."

"Your love for me was not healthy?" you ask.
And I tell you,
"I depended upon you for too much
Without you,
I couldn't stand
I couldn't stand on my own
I needed you more than I should have
And I needed to lose you
To realize I could pick myself up on my own."
"So you do not need me anymore?" you question me.
Your eyes drop my gaze.
"Of course I do.
I need you.
And I can let you have me,
I can let you consume me,
Because now I know that even if I have you,
I still have myself too."
Your eyes clear up
And you run your finger across my cheek
"You can do it on your own then,
But you don't want to?"
Your words bring a smile to my face
And I grab onto your hand on my cheek
Lacing my fingers through yours
"No, I want to go through these things with you."
You look away from me
Your eyes searching through your thoughts
"This is from our conversation from before, correct?
That we are meant to go through life with one another.

A common breath.
Sharing the most important moments as one."
I think back to our conversation,
All of our conversations
And I think of all of the things we shared with each other,
Promised each other,
We are finally living out those promises.
We are just two people
Madly in love
Finally understanding the meaning behind all our shared
words.

92.

I'm walking down the aisle toward you
Keeping my eyes locked on yours
You suck in a breath
And I can tell you're going to cry
But you can't
Because if you start,
I will too.
You only look to me
And I can't see anyone else
I just see you
Waiting
For me
To bind yourself to me,
Forever
To allow me to be yours,
Always
And I feel like I'm dreaming
The closer I get to you, the more unreal it all feels
Finally coming together,
Together to be joined as one
I can't even smile
My eyes are locked onto yours,

Those blue eyes.
You grab onto my hands
And I hear someone start talking
But I don't really hear them
My focus is solely on you
Your beautiful eyes
The way a smile pulls at your lips as you look down at me.
My insides heat up under your gaze.
In a tux, you look unlike anything I've seen in this world
But you don't even seem to notice
How beautiful you are
How beautiful your soul is
And the craziest part is you're giving me that soul
And that's why I can't hear anything else
I just see you
Since the first moment you kissed me
I've always only ever seen you
Just you.

93.

I'm moving through the water
In the warm Adriatic you once dreamed of taking me to
And a little boy comes running up behind me
I turn, hearing him splash,
And he jumps into my arms
He holds onto me, and I hold onto him.
With the sun in my eyes,
I scan the beach
And find you easily.
You're tossing a little girl into the air
Her giggles permeate across the sand,
And out to me.
It makes my insides light up as though the sun is being
housed within me.
I look into the boy's eyes, and I am greeted with my own.
As the little girl is set on the ground,
She runs toward me
Unsteady at first, but she gets her footing
And it's as though she has taken flight
She runs to me with such determination
And as I scoop her into my arms,
I'm greeted with your eyes

Those blue eyes.
You come up behind her,
And you look at me
In exactly the same way you always have
And always will.
Your eyes are filled with love,
Watching me hold the two little products of our love in my
arms.
A smile on your face.
A smile on mine.

About the Author

Kenzie Hart graduated from the University of South Florida with a degree in Interdisciplinary Social Sciences: History and International Studies. She is currently living abroad and pursuing her Masters Degree. She usually can be found at the local coffee shop writing, reading, or planning her next adventure.

Follow her website at www.kenziehart.net

99018968R00155

Made in the USA
Columbia, SC
05 July 2018